W9-DJK-686

The Catholic
Theological Union
LIBRARY
Chicago, Ill.
WITHDRAWN

MORAL PRINCIPLES *of* NURSING

MORAL PRINCIPLES *of* NURSING

Reverend Edward J. Hayes

Reverend Paul J. Hayes

Dorothy Ellen Kelly, R.N.

THE MACMILLAN COMPANY, NEW YORK
COLLIER-MACMILLAN LIMITED, LONDON

Nihil Obstat: Aloysius J. Welsh, S.T.D.
Censor Librorum

Imprimatur: ✠ Thomas A. Boland, S.T.D.
Archbishop of Newark
June 17, 1963

First Printing

Library of Congress catalog card number: 64-12859

The Macmillan Company, New York
Collier-Macmillan Canada, Ltd., Toronto, Ontario

Printed in the United States of America

designed by Mary A. Brown

TO THE PATRONESS OF NURSES

Our Lady of Perpetual Help

Preface

Every nurse, whether Catholic or non-Catholic, is frequently confronted with ethical problems. Many others engaged in hospital work and the care of the sick, such as priests, teachers, and hospital administrators, are also concerned with medico-moral problems. This book presents the answers to such problems as taught by the Catholic Church.

The conscientious Catholic nurse will seek a solution for ethical problems that is in harmony with the laws of God as expounded by her Church, which is the authoritative interpreter of divine law. "She will not fulfill this obligation," says Father Francis J. Connell, "by merely resolving to consult a priest whenever a problem arises; for sometimes she must act at once, without an opportunity to seek advice. She must be familiar with the principles of ethics pertinent to her professional tasks, and be able to apply them herself to the cases she is likely to encounter."

Moral Principles of Nursing provides this information in clear and simple language, furnishing a course for the student nurse and a well-indexed reference book for all concerned. The glossary of medical and theological terms will be helpful to the student, and the cases for discussion and problems for solution at the end of each chapter will assist in effective teaching. The use of charts to illustrate various moral applications is new to the field, having been first introduced by the authors in their *Moral Handbook of Nursing*. To help the nurse keep constantly in mind the supernatural motives that should animate her, some brief and inspiring prayers for various occasions have been added, as well as material on the character of a nurse.

The experience of the authors includes years of ministrations to the sick, as well as lecturing and teaching in both diploma and degree schools of nursing. This experience has been brought to bear upon the text.

To assist the instructor in making a realistic adjustment of the course to the number of hours available, we offer the following suggestions:

In a course of 45 hours, the entire book may be covered.

For a 30-hour course, stress Chapters 1, 4, 6, 7, 8, 9, 10, and 11.

In a 15-hour course, stress Chapters 4, 6, 7, 8, 9, and 11.

If only an hour or two is alloted, the presentation should be focused on the material in Chapter 11.

Under "References for Further Study" we have included, in addition to the most recent works, a number of older books and periodicals, because they contain useful material and are still available.

Pope Pius XII, addressing a group of nurses, reflected a deep interest in the vocation of nursing and a keen awareness of its demands when he spoke these words: "It is our earnest desire that you gain an ever-clearer knowledge of your responsibilities and an ever-more-ardent will to carry them out fully." This twofold objective expresses the mind of all those truly interested in the profession and states concisely the ultimate purpose of the authors in writing this book.

Rev. Edward J. Hayes
Rev. Paul J. Hayes
Dorothy Ellen Kelly, R.N.

Acknowledgment

The authors owe a particular debt of thanks to their revered friend, The Very Reverend Francis J. Connell, C.Ss.R., of the Catholic University of America, who gave abundantly of his time, experience, and knowledge in the preparation of this book. His advice was especially valuable in the application of moral principles to recent medical trends and techniques.

Beloved daughters, near and far, we speak to you with all our heart. You are the devoted helpers of Christ in His mystical members. He is ill, and is entrusted to your motherly hands, to your feminine delicacy, to your spirit of devotion, to the intuition you so happily possess of sensing requirements in the face of human distress, to your heart which realizes how a soul suffers when the body is in pain. Since Jesus is in every sick person, however corrupt, however ignorant of Him, you are to Him what kind and hospitable Martha was, and compassionate Veronica, and the pious women of Jerusalem. What you cannot do for Jesus in your mystical encounters with Him in Holy Communion, you can do in the wards of your hospitals, in the sacred precincts of your clinics.

PIUS XII

POPE OF MEDICINE

Address to Catholic Nurses,
July 19, 1939

Contents

IN APPEARANCE, MORAL DEMANDS ARE A
CURB. IN REALITY, THEY MAKE THEIR
OWN CONTRIBUTION TO THE BETTER AND
NOBLER ACHIEVEMENTS PRODUCED BY MAN
FOR THE BENEFIT OF SCIENCE, OF THE
INDIVIDUAL, AND OF THE COMMUNITY.

PIUS XII

Address to the First International Congress of Histopathology

PART I

Basic Principles of Ethics

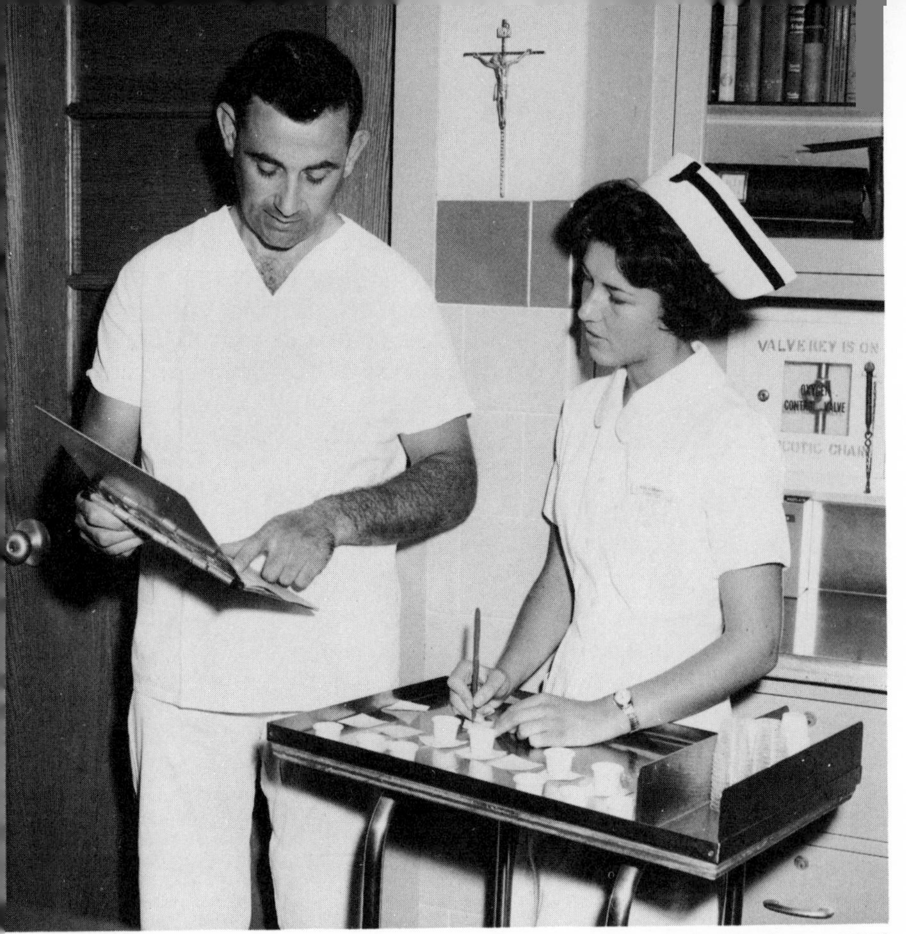

(DAVIDAN PHOTO.)

Holy Name Hospital, Teaneck, New Jersey.

CHAPTER I

The Nature of Ethics

The science of ethics · Ethics and the Catholic Church · The norm of morality · The role of the moralist

THE FUNDAMENTAL GUIDING PRINCIPLE which governs the conduct of all men has been given in the twofold rule laid down by Christ: love of God and love of neighbor. This norm should be uppermost in the mind of every nurse. But this is a general guiding principle that must be spelled out. How in my life am I to express my love of God? How am I as a nurse in concrete daily activity to put into practice love of neighbor? A simple answer might be given by saying that we do so by keeping the Commandments. But this also is general. The science called "ethics" spells out obligations in specific terms. In this book, moral obligations and ideals as they relate to the nursing profession will be thoroughly discussed. These moral norms, far from being viewed as burdensome duties, will take on a new aspect in the day-to-day life of the nurse if they are seen as specific vital application of the generic norm of Christ, love of God and love of neighbor.

The Science of Ethics

Ethics is the science which guides our judgment concerning the morality of human acts. Medical ethics is the particular aspect of the science of ethics which guides our judgment concerning the goodness or badness of human acts in the medical profession.

We may narrow the field further and speak of "nursing ethics." This book confines itself to the study of nursing ethics. Of course, frequently the ethical problems of the doctor and nurse overlap, but in this work we do not directly treat of problems that are purely those of the physician.

It should be made clear at the outset that medical ethics is concerned with moral principles. Often there is confusion on this point because medical ethics is sometimes considered as dealing primarily with medical etiquette. Medical ethics correctly understood deals with *moral conduct*, a subject far more necessary and vital than etiquette in the life of a nurse.

Ethics and Moral Theology

Ethics is a *natural* science. It employs the power of human reason, which is purely a natural process. It is not based on the teachings of the Catholic Church, nor is it based on the Bible. Being a branch of philosophy, it arrives at its conclusions by the use of human reason, which is philosophy's only tool.

Ethics is a *practical* science. It is not studied purely for the love of learning. All are bound in conscience to apply its principles to their conduct.

Ethics is not a physical science. It does not deal with physical laws, such as "Water seeks its own level." It is rather a *moral* science, dealing with the free acts of men.

The *material object* of a science is the matter with which the science deals. In the case of ethics, the material object consists of *human acts*. Human acts are acts performed by a man as a man—acts in which his superior faculties of both intellect and will are used—as opposed to those acts which man performs in common with animal and vegetative life.

The *formal object* of a science is the precise aspect under which that science deals with its subject matter. In the case of ethics, the formal object is the *moral rectitude* of man's human acts in relation to man's natural end.

In order to reach its conclusions, ethics draws upon the following *sources:*

1. Human reason (primary source)
2. Experience
   a. Personal experience
   b. Experience of others
      1) Contemporary
      2) Historical

Note that divine revelation (the Bible and the teachings of the Church) does not appear among the sources. Divine revelation is not a source of ethics but is employed as a check on its conclusions. If some apparent conclusion of ethics is contrary to God's revelation, then the conclusion must be wrong, since God cannot contradict Himself.

Ethics is also called *moral philosophy*. It is distinct from moral theology, although they bear a close relationship to each other. Ethics is based on human reason alone, which looks only to a natural end, while moral theology is based on faith as well as reason and recognizes a supernatural end.

The material object of moral theology (the matter with which moral theology deals) is the human act—the same material object as ethics. The formal object of moral theology, however, is the morality of the human act in relation to man's supernatural end.

As God actually decreed things, man cannot choose a natural end but must strive for a supernatural end.

The sources which moral theology utilizes are these:

1. Divine revelation as interpreted by the Catholic Church
2. Human reason
3. Experience

The valid conclusions of the science of ethics regarding our conduct are accepted and confirmed by moral theology, which never contradicts the correct conclusions of human reason. The entire natural science of ethics is elevated and perfected by the supernatural science of moral theology.

In practice, medical ethics is studied in conjunction with moral theology. In this way the conclusions of human reason are verified and confirmed by the teachings of divine revelation. Such courses are sometimes called "moral ethics."

Difference Between Ethics and Morals

Ethics is the science which guides our judgment concerning the morality of human acts. "Morals" is human conduct in the light of ethics. Ethics is a science of ideals; morals is the application of ethics. It is therefore entirely possible for a nurse to have good ethics and bad morals. Her principles are correct, but she fails to apply them. Accurate ethical principles and good moral conduct are both necessary in a nurse. It is desirable then that she strive diligently to train her mind so that she may have good ethics and at the same time train her will so that she may have good morals.

Basis of Ethics

The science of ethics is based upon the acceptance of the following truths:

1. Human reason is capable of discovering some truths.
2. God exists.
3. God is just.
4. A good life shall merit God's reward.
5. An evil life shall merit God's punishment.
6. Man has a soul.
7. Man's soul is immortal.
8. Man's soul has the faculties of intellect and will.
9. The object of the intellect is truth.
10. The object of the will is goodness.

11. Man's will is free and is therefore capable of moral good or moral evil.

12. Good must be done; evil must be avoided.

13. An act is good when it is in conformity with right reason.

14. An act is evil when it is not in conformity with right reason.

These truths are proved in other branches of philosophy. In accepting them, the science of ethics does not show itself incapable of proving them but merely leaves their proof to the departments of philosophy which are properly concerned with them. Each physical science accepts numerous facts established by other sciences. Engineering accepts mathematics; medicine accepts biology. In like manner, ethics accepts the fundamental truths which we have listed.

Ethics and the Catholic Church

Although ethics uses as its only tool the light of human reason, nevertheless the student of nursing ethics can find great help in the moral teachings of Almighty God as revealed in the Written Word of God and in Tradition as interpreted and explained in the living teaching authority of God's Church. Having arrived at the principles of nursing ethics by human reason, we will often discover that our conclusions are already taught by divine revelation. Medical ethics in practice, as Catholics understand it, is not merely a philosophical science but a supernatural moral science and as such is subject to the authority of the Church.

Catholics believe that Jesus Christ, the Son of God, established the Catholic Church for the purpose of saving souls. They further believe that God's eternal law is the basis of every just law, and that it is by means of obedience to law that souls are saved. Therefore the Catholic Church is perforce intensely interested in every law, be it natural or positive, ecclesiastical or civil. Indeed, the Church is more than merely interested. Having been appointed by Jesus Christ, the Son of God, with the divine charge of winning souls to Him, the Church is positively obliged to guide men in the understanding of His law and to urge men to obey it. Moreover, since God has so charged and directed His Church, He will, because of His love and solicitude for souls, enlighten the Church in the proper and correct interpretation of His law. Indeed, He promised this help to His apostles and their successors when He told them that He would be with them at all times as long as the world would last.

It follows, then, that the Catholic Church possesses the authority to interpret all law insofar as it affects the salvation of souls.

These principles apply no less to the laws of medical ethics than to any other laws. By obedience to the principles of medical ethics with the proper supernatural motive, it is possible to win a higher place in the kingdom of God; by disobedience to them, it is possible for a man to lose his soul. The Catholic Church is greatly interested in the principles of medical and nursing ethics by reason of her interest in the salvation of men's souls. The Church does not hesitate to interpret these principles with authority when she deems it necessary for the good of those over whom she has been given charge by Christ.

God is the Author not only of those laws which govern the conduct of men but also of those laws which govern the operation of the physical universe. Since God cannot contradict Himself, the findings of science must at all times be in agreement with the conclusions of sound philosophy and theology. There can be no contradiction between moral and ethical principles on the one hand and principles of physical science on the other: God is the Author of both. They are complementary to each other. Medicine and morals can and should go hand in hand.

Pope Pius XII has said:

> Although the Christian applauds new scientific discoveries and makes use of them, he rejects all materialism's exaggerated glorification of science and culture. He knows that science and culture occupy a place on the scale of objective values, but that, while they are not the lowest, neither are they the highest. In their regard, too, he repeats today

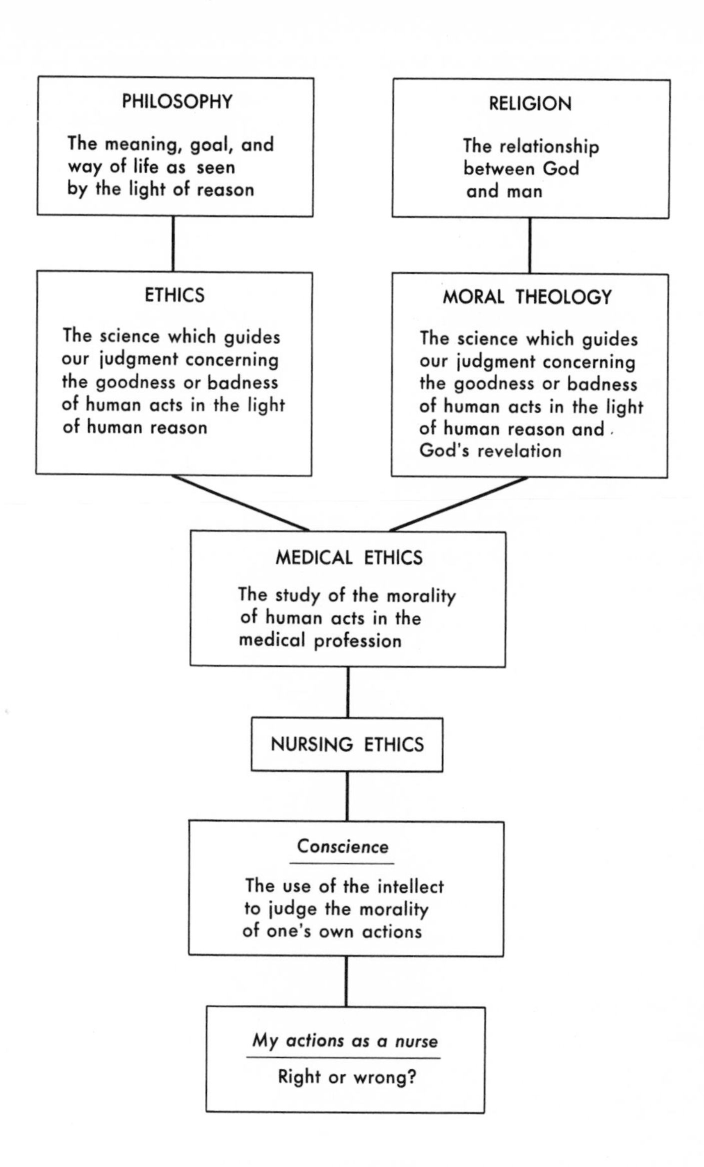

Figure 1. Moral judgment.

as ever and always: "Make it your first care to find the kingdom of God, and his approval" (Matt. 6:33). The highest, the ultimate value for man is to be found, not in science or its technical capabilities, but in the love of God and devotion to his service.[1]

The Norm of Morality

There exists an intrinsic and essential difference between moral good and moral evil. This seems like a simple and acceptable statement of fact until we begin to analyze the motives and guiding norms being used by many people today.

There are some who use the norm that *current opinions and customs* determine the acceptable mode of acting or at least rationalize along those lines. This is reflected in the not uncommonly heard phrase "Everybody is doing it." But right is still right no matter how many people are wrong. Many of the attempts at persuasive arguments relative to "planned parenthood" and contraceptive birth control run along this line: Most people today hold that contraception is morally allowable; therefore it is. In other words, there are people who would in point of fact base morality on majority opinion.

Again, some people in our day consider as good and moral those things which in their opinion help society or others. This is a form of *warped altruism.* Euthanasia is "justified" since it relieves a person of his suffering and relieves society and a family of a burden.

Other people regulate their actions in accordance with what is useful for them at the moment rather than what is objectively right or wrong. This is the norm of *expediency*. One of the best examples of a man who used this standard is the one who sat in the judgment seat passing a sentence on an innocent Man nineteen hundred years ago. It was Pilate who said of Christ, "I have no part in the death of this innocent man." But because he knew that the people might have him removed from his office if he did not do their will he sentenced Christ to death; it was more advanta-

[1] Address to obstetricians and gynecologists, Jan. 8, 1956.

geous to him to do so at the time. It was the expedient thing to do. Many a person today guides his actions by expediency rather than by morality. Not infrequently in modern times rulers of nations have abandoned the ship of state to the winds and currents of expediency, with results always confusing, frequently dangerous, and sometimes disastrous. This way of reasoning is sometimes called "situation ethics."

There are still others who act in accordance with what is *more desirable,* what one "prefers" doing rather than what is right or wrong. Such is the man who has bad teeth but will not go to the dentist; he has no doubts about what he ought to do, but a visit to the dentist may be unpleasant. This standard when applied to God's law is dangerous, for such a person will attempt to justify principles and a course of action which find no justification in the teaching of Christ. Such is the nurse who knows that she should in certain particular circumstances express disapproval of an immoral procedure or refuse to cooperate in an immoral operation but would find this unpleasant and so compromises her principles.

Morality is not a matter of current opinions or actions of the majority; it is not a matter of what is useful at the moment, of a spirit of altruism, of expediency, of feeling. It is not a matter of social usefulness or sentiment. *That is right which is in conformity with human nature and right reason or commanded by God; that is wrong which runs contrary to human nature, right reason, or God's commands.* Rape, murder, and adultery are wrong not because of statistics or popularity or public apathy or expediency or opinion polls, but because they run counter to right reason and God's will. Basically, it is a question of principle versus expediency.

Morality is intrinsic, objective, and unchanging. That is right which is in conformity with the divine will. It is expressed in our life through a properly formed conscience.

A nurse must cultivate an analytical mind. She cannot allow her moral sense to be clouded by false norms of morality with which she will be surrounded. She must train herself to get to the basic norm of right and wrong and guide her actions accordingly.

The Role of the Moralist

It is important to alert the student against any misunderstanding regarding the moral teaching of the Catholic Church. It is not common for the Church to issue decrees or moral decisions regarding medical minutiae. The Church teaches moral principles and usually leaves the narrower application to qualified moralists, who are sometimes specialists in particular fields, such as medicine, and who are known as "approved authors." Even the ordinary moral discourses of the Pope, such as those he might give to the groups of physicians or nurses who visit him from time to time, do not of themselves constitute ultimate and final ecclesiastical decisions. Rather they are the instructions of the supreme teacher and moralist of the Church, worthy as such of the most profound and reverent consideration, even though not intended as infallible pronouncements.

Therefore if anyone were to ask, for example, "What is the official teaching of the Holy See on induction of labor?" the answer, strictly speaking, would be "Nothing." If this sounds strange, consider the parallel question: "What is the official teaching of the medical profession on the induction of labor?" Of course, there is no direct answer to that question or any other like it. A physician who attempted to reply would find himself quoting authorities. He would point out that there are various opinions on certain aspects of the problem, and that there is room for a difference of opinion. In practice, a doctor could not be criticized if he followed a well-founded opinion of any recognized expert.

The moral parallel is clear and understandable. In writing on the moral aspects of medical matters, we are usually not quoting some official Vatican document but rather making a reasoned application of moral principles, basing our conclusions on the well-founded opinions of approved moralists in light of certain medical trends. In practice, a nurse's actions are in conformity with the moral teachings of the Catholic Church if she is following a well-founded opinion of any approved author.

Topics for Discussion

Items may be true, partly true, erroneous, or unsolvable. First judge, then discuss.

1. Religion is all right in its place, but it certainly has nothing to do with a strictly physical science like medicine.
2. Catholic nurses are torn between the conclusions of science and the laws of the Church.
3. Christ's law of love of neighbor is less applicable in a modern capitalistic society then it was in His day.
4. Ethics presupposes belief in the existence of God. Some people do not believe in God. These people need not live according to an ethical or moral code.
5. A nurse working in a nonsectarian hospital cannot at all times follow ethics.
6. In these modern days we are living in a rapidly changing world. Moral principles should be adjusted to apply to present-day situations.
7. We should leave the Catholic Church out of the study of medical ethics, which is not a sectarian matter.
8. The more you study ethics, the more obligations you have. The less you study ethics, the fewer obligations you have. Why multiply obligations? The Ten Commandments are enough.

Cases for Solution

1. A Catholic student in a non-Catholic nursing school can easily take a course in ethics, which is given by a priest of a nearby parish. However, she arbitrarily decides against taking the course. Is she guilty of a moral fault of negligence?
2. A Catholic doctor often expresses contempt for the medico-moral teachings of Pope Pius XII on the grounds that they are not part of the teachings of Christ. Is the doctor morally wrong?
3. A young non-Catholic nursing student determines that she will never read a Catholic ethics book for fear she might learn some ideas that will bind her conscience. Has she escaped all moral burdens by this device?

References for Further Study

Bourke, V. J. *Ethics: A Textbook in Moral Philosophy*, New York: The Macmillan Company, 1953.

Connell, Francis J. *Morals in Politics and Professions*, Westminster, Md.: The Newman Press, 1951.

Healy, Edwin F. *Moral Guidance*, Chicago: Loyola University Press, 1960.

McFadden, Charles J. *Medical Ethics*, Philadelphia: F. A. Davis Company, 1961.

(TARGET PHOTOS.)

Holy Name Hospital, Teaneck, New Jersey.

CHAPTER 2

The Morality of Human Acts

Elements determining morality · Principles for judging morality · Conditions affecting morality · Other factors affecting the voluntary nature of human actions · Cautions regarding moral judgment · Occasions of sin

A human act is one that proceeds from the deliberate free will of man. It is an act that is deliberately and knowingly performed by one having the use of reason. Therefore, both intellect and will are in play. It is an act proper to man as man. For example, if a man decides that he needs a little exercise and so goes for a walk, he is performing a human act. Again, when a nurse, following instructions, administers medications to a patient, she performs a human act.

Quite different from a human act is an act of man. *An act of man is one that is not dependent upon intellect and free will.* It is done by a human person but is not proper to him as a person because it does not stem from those faculties which are peculiar to man, namely, intellect and will. In plain language, an act of man is essentially an animal act. If a man walks in his sleep, he performs not a human act but merely an act of man. All the acts of a human infant are acts of man because an infant does not have the use of reason; in other words, his intellect is not functioning. Breathing is an act of man. So also is the spontaneous recoiling from the approach of a dangerous and fast-moving object, such as flying glass in an accident.

In judging the morality of acts (whether they are good or

evil), obviously we are concerned only with human acts. The moral law has nothing directly to do with acts of man.

Elements Determining Morality

Every human act derives its morality from three elements: *the act itself* (which moralists technically call "the object"), *the purpose of the act* (sometimes called "the end"), and the *circumstances surrounding the act.* Moralists refer to these three elements as "object, end, and circumstance." In language less technical, we shall refer to them as "act, purpose, and circumstances."

The Act Itself

It will be seen rather easily that, in order to judge the morality of a human act, we must first consider the act itself. Visiting a sick man would seem, on the face of it, to be morally good. Certainly it is good as far as the act itself is concerned. Circumstances or purpose might make it evil, but the act itself is a good one. On the other hand, stabbing one's father with a knife is in itself a bad act, although it is possible to imagine circumstances when it would be morally allowable. When the police arrive at the scene of an assignment in response to a call, they are forced to make a hasty judgment based upon the act itself. If you were walking down the street eating an apple and a neighbor called the police and made a complaint against you, he would have to do a lot of talking to persuade the police to arrest you. On the other hand, if you have just turned in a false alarm of fire, the act itself is sufficient for an arrest. As for your allegedly good purpose, you will have to explain that to the judge at a later date. As in the legal order, so in the moral order; in passing judgment on the moral goodness or badness of any act, the first point to be considered is the act itself. That is what moralists mean when they say we must examine the "object."

It is well to note that moral judgment must be based not only on the physical aspect of an act but also and primarily on its moral aspect. If a man tells a lie, the moralist must base his judgment not on the physical act of uttering words but rather on the telling of an untruth.

Purpose

Now let us consider the purpose, or end, of an act. *The purpose of a human act is the reason for which the act is performed.* In other words, the purpose is the intention of the agent. A man lies about a doctor for the purpose of destroying the doctor's reputation. A nurse lies to a patient because she fears that the truth will disturb his peace of mind. In each case, a lie was told, but obviously the guilt is radically different. What changed it? The purpose of the agent.

It should be observed that the purpose will not always change the morality of an act because some acts are intrinsically wrong (evil by their nature). Take for instance the act of murder, which is the unjust taking of human life. A murderer may argue that he had a good purpose, such as the elimination of a habitual thief; but the murder is still wrong. Both civil law and moral law follow the same line of thought on matters like this because the reasoning is based on the very laws of nature.

Circumstances

There is an old saying, "Circumstances alter cases." That is true, and that is why the morality of a human act must be judged in the light of the circumstances. From the moral point of view, *the circumstances of a human act are those factors, distinct from the act itself and from the purpose, which may affect the morality of the act.* Setting fire to a house at night is worse than by day, because the circumstance of darkness and the fact that the occupants are sleeping radically increase the guilt of the arsonist. Murder, however evil, is so frequent these days that the average case causes very little public excitement. But if it were reported that the President of the nation had been murdered by his wife while he was delivering an address to the Senate, undoubtedly there would be universal excitement. The basic fact was the same; A man was killed. But the circumstances were radically different. Consider the hypothetical case of a nurse who tells an obscene joke to her classmate, then to a high school boy who is in the hospital visiting his mother. For the first of these offenses, the authorities would probably take no action; for the latter, she might well lose her position. Circumstances alter cases. Any careful moral judgment will weigh the circumstances.

For this reason, it is often impossible to give a direct and explicit answer to a moral question that specifies no circumstances. Priests are frequently asked, "Is kissing a sin?" That requires several other questions, such as, Who is being kissed? By whom? Why? Another favorite question is, "May a divorced woman receive Communion?" No priest can give a fast yes or no to that question because it depends entirely on circumstances. The student should expect that instructors, be they doctors, nurses, or priests, will at times parry a question with another question. This is not necessarily an evasion. It is usually an attempt to obtain circumstantial information, without which an accurate answer would be impossible.

Principles for Judging Morality

Various fundamental principles must be applied in judging the morality of a specific act. We list here certain of these principles that should particularly be kept in mind.

1. An act is morally good if the act itself, the purpose, and the circumstances are substantially good. We say "substantially" good because an act may have minor moral shortcomings and still be a truly good act. A Catholic who obeys the fast laws of his Church during Lent, even though because of vanity he also wants to lose a little weight, is still performing a good act in fasting. (The philosophical term for such a minor shortcoming would be an "accidental" defect, the term opposed to "substantial.")

2. If an act itself is intrinsically evil (evil by its very nature), *the act is not morally allowable regardless of purpose or circum-*

stances. Murder is intrinsically evil; therefore it is never allowed as the solution to a problem, no matter how grave.

3. *If an act is itself morally good or at least indifferent, its morality will be judged by the purpose or circumstances.* Walking is in itself indifferent. If a person is walking for exercise to renew his energy for work, he is doing something good. If he is walking into a store to commit an act of theft, he is doing something morally evil.

4. *Circumstances may create, mitigate, or aggravate sin.* They may change an indifferent act into one that is morally sinful. For instance, striking a match is in itself an indifferent act, but striking a match in the presence of explosive vapor may be suicide or murder or both. To read a wholesome book when one should be caring for a patient is morally wrong. Circumstances may compound the sinfulness of an act. Fornication (sexual relations with an unmarried person) is a grave sin against purity. Adultery (sexual relations with a married person) is a twofold grave sin, against purity and against justice to the innocent spouse. To blaspheme is sinful; to do it in front of children adds a sin of scandal. Circumstances may make a mortal (grave) sin out of a venial (slight) sin, or a venial sin out of a mortal sin. To steal five dollars is ordinarily a light sin; to steal the same amount from a very poor person is a serious sin.

5. *If all three moral elements* (the act itself, purpose, and circumstances) *are good, the act is good. If any one element is evil, the act is evil.* If a reservoir is fed by three streams and one is polluted, the reservoir is polluted. An automobile that is in perfect condition except for a leak in the exhaust system is not a good automobile. A man who never does a thing wrong except to rob banks is not a good man but a bad one.

Conditions Affecting Morality

We are responsible before God only for truly human acts. Knowledge and free will must play a part. If they do not, we have not a human act but only an act of man. The objective goodness or badness of an act is one thing; the subjective accountability of the agent is another. It is easy enough for us to agree that the act of murder is bad. But just how guilty before God this murderer is, here and now, is a very difficult question.

Since free will and knowledge always play a part in moral guilt, anything which might interfere with free will and/or knowledge must be considered in making a prudent judgment concerning the morality of an action. There are five particular conditions which may lessen or even remove moral responsibility: ignorance, fear, concupiscence, violence, and habit. These we shall now examine one by one.

Ignorance

In general, *ignorance is lack of knowledge in a person capable of knowing*. In some cases we are responsible for knowledge, in other cases we are not; in other words, there are different types of ignorance. Before we can explain the moral principles regarding ignorance, we must distinguish the various types.

"*Ignorance of the law*" *is lack of knowledge that a particular law exists*, as when a driver does not know there is a 60-mile-per-hour speed limit for a particular road.

"*Ignorance of the fact*" *is lack of realization that one is violating a law*, as when a driver knows that there is a 60-mile-per-hour limit but does not realize that he is traveling at 70.

"*Vincible ignorance*" *is that which can and should be dispelled.* It implies culpable negligence. The subject could know and ought to know.

"*Simple vincible ignorance*" *is present when one makes some, but not sufficient, effort to dispel his ignorance.* Suppose a nurse is unsure of dosage. She refers to the doctor's order sheet and finds that she is unable to read his writing. She knows the doctor is at his office but does not bother to call him. As she administers the medication, guessing at the dosage, she is guilty of simple vincible ignorance.

"*Crass vincible ignorance*" *is that which results from a mere lack of effort.* Let us suppose that a moral problem arises for an operating supervisor. On the shelf over her desk is a good medical ethics book with an excellent index which could quickly solve the problem. However, she does not bother. She is in crass vincible ignorance.

"*Affected vincible ignorance*" *is that which is deliberately fostered in order to avoid any obligation that knowledge might bring to light.* Let us imagine a nurse who accepts employment with

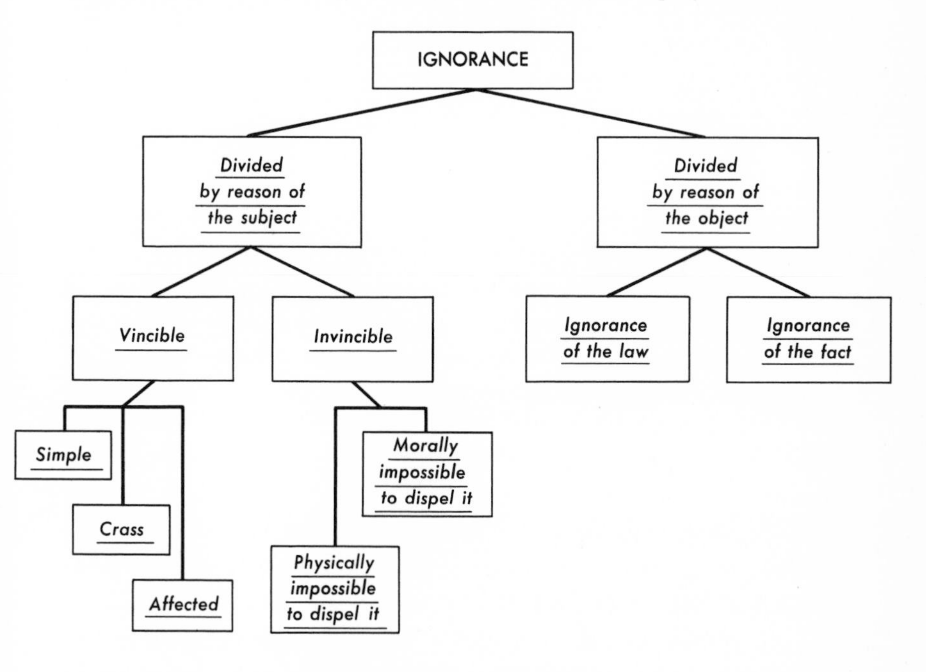

Figure 2. Types of ignorance.

a doctor who frequently practices artificial insemination. She may suspect that this is immoral but carefully avoids inquiring or even discussing the matter with anybody, lest she discover that she is cooperating in immorality and be obliged to leave her well-paying job. She is guilty of affected vincible ignorance. It is affected because she wants to be ignorant, and it is vincible because she could dispel the ignorance easily.

"*Invincible ignorance*" *is that which cannot be dispelled.* This situation may exist either because the individual is unable to secure adequate information, even after a reasonable effort, or because he simply does not know that there is any problem—in other words he is ignorant of his ignorance. The person cannot be expected to take steps to enlighten himself because he is unaware that he is in need of any enlightenment. For example, a certain nurses' aide customarily tells lies by way of making excuses for minor faults and feels that, since they harm no one, they are in no way sinful. She is ignorant of the fact that she is in need of enlightenment on the point. Another individual may be somewhat troubled in mind about a

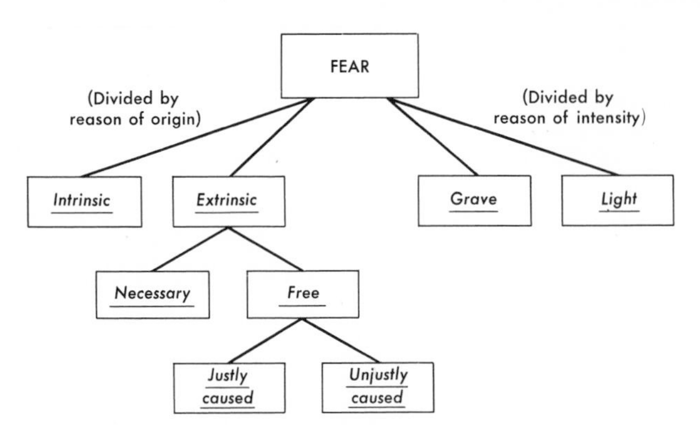

Figure 3. Types of fear.

situation. After having made a reasonable effort to dispel his ignorance, and having failed to dispel it, he may proceed to perform the act. Let us suppose that a group of students are due to return to the nurses' home by 10:30 P.M. They are enjoying themselves and decide to return 15 minutes late. One of them, a freshman, wonders if this infraction might be a sin and asks the opinion of two seniors who are present. They say that they have no idea about the morality of such things. Having no way to dispel her ignorance, she would not sin by staying out the extra few minutes. Of course, if the case is likely to occur again, a competent advisor should be consulted at the earliest convenient time. But once a reasonable effort has been made, as of that particular time, the ignorance is invincible.

MORAL PRINCIPLES CONCERNING IGNORANCE. The moral principles concerning the effect of ignorance upon a human act may be summed up briefly. *Invincible ignorance eliminates responsibility. Vincible ignorance does not eliminate moral responsibility but lessens it.*[1] As an example of vincible ignorance, let us take the case of a doctor who is uncertain as to the treatment indicated for his patient's ailment. He has books at hand that will give him the answer, but he does not consult them because he is busy. His ignorance is vincible, so he is guilty of a moral fault, but not so guilty as he would be if he deliberately and knowingly gave the patient a medication not appropriate to the complaint.

Fear

Fear is an agitation or disturbance of mind resulting from some present or imminent danger. It is one of the emotions.

There are several types of fear. *Light fear is fear in which the evil threatening is either present-but-slight or grave-but-remote.* An elderly lady experiences fear when she hears someone passing her door at night, but her fear is only slight because she knows it is probably her neighbor arriving home earlier than usual. This is what we mean by a present-but-slight threatening evil. For a grave-but-remote threatening evil, we may give this example: A man fears that he may die of cancer later in life, but his fear is light because the grave danger is very remote.

Grave fear is that which is present when the evil threatening is considered as serious.

Intrinsic grave fear is that agitation of the mind which arises because of a disposition within one's own mind or body. The fear of cancer is intrinsic fear.

Extrinisic fear is that agitation of the mind which arises from something outside oneself. Under this heading come *necessary extrinsic fear* (that arising because of some external physical law of nature, such as fear when a house is on fire) and *free extrinsic fear* (that arising from the free will of some other person, such as fear of a robber in a house). Free extrinsic fear may be *justly caused*, such

[1] Authorities differ on the moral responsibility arising from affected ignorance.

as a murderer's fear of being executed, or *unjustly caused*, such as a nurse's fear of being dismissed if she does not cooperate in an immoral operation.

MORAL PRINCIPLES CONCERNING FEAR. The moral principles concerning fear are summed up in this axiom: *Fear diminishes the voluntary nature of an act.*

One distinction should be kept in mind. Some acts are done because of fear. The act would not have been done had fear not been present. Some acts, on the other hand, are done with fear present but would have been done anyway. Any acts which are done, and would have been done, whether fear was present or not are clearly voluntary, and if they are morally wrong, the person is morally responsible. This norm is usually clearly seen and accepted. But beyond this, those acts which are done only because of fear are in reality freely willed and so beget moral responsibility. However, a sinful act done because of fear is somewhat less free and therefore less sinful than an act done not under the influence of fear. Let us suppose that a nurse gives some narcotics illegally to a hospital employee, fearing violence at his hands if she does not comply with his demand. Her act is free, but she is less morally responsible than if fear were not present.

Concupiscence

Concupiscence is the rebellion of the passions against reason. Or, to put it another way, it is a tendency of human nature toward evil.[2] Concupiscence is the revolt of the sense faculties of man against the dominion of his higher faculty of reason. All men perceive this revolt within themselves. There are times when we feel strongly drawn to do something that we know would cause nothing but sorrow and regret to all concerned, even to ourselves, and yet we are drawn to do it. We seem at times to be like a man driving a team of unruly horses, which pull in different directions and threaten to

[2] Although the word "concupiscence" is frequently used in the Bible to indicate moral evil, some theologians use the term simply in the sense of an inclination of a sensitive appetite toward its object.

upset the wagon. Who is there who has not performed some regrettable act and then asked himself the question, "Why did I do it?" Even great men speak of this internal conflict. "My own actions bewilder me," says Saint Paul, "What I do is not what I wish to do, but something which I hate" (Romans 7:15).

The passions may be defined as the sense appetites of human nature reaching out toward their objects. Under this heading would come love, hatred, joy, grief, desire, aversion, hope, courage, fear, and anger. A nurse often observes that a person who has had a prolonged stay in the hospital and suffered much pain may feel discouraged. This is one of the emotions of which we speak.

The passions are not in themselves evil. Parents may and often should exercise a just anger in order to discipline their children. Christ, who was able to hurl forth the challenge, "Can any of you convict me of sin?" (John 8:46), displayed a fearful anger when He rebuked His enemies and when He drove the money changers out of the temple. The sex passion, occasion of so much heartbreak, crime, and sorrow, is when properly used the means of giving citizens to the nation and saints to heaven. *The passions are not in themselves evil. They are, however, in revolt against our nobler self; and that revolt is called concupiscence.*

Obviously, an evil action performed in the heat of passion is different—perhaps quite different—from an evil action that is calculated. Civil law recognizes this fact in making a distinction between first- and second-degree murder. Judges often take concupiscence into consideration when they hear a case, although they may not use the theological term for it. Such recognition of the fact of concupiscence is well founded, for it does have an influence upon the morality of human acts. Sometimes it happens that an individual deliberately arouses his passions. In such a case, moral culpability is increased rather than lessened. If, on the other hand, passion is spontaneous, culpability is lessened. A young man who deliberately reads an obscene book before a date increases the guilt of the immorality that takes place on the date. A young man who is leading a good life and is surprised by an unexpected temptation when on a date may possibly be less guilty in yielding to temptation under the pressure of concupiscence.

Concupiscence may be divided into two types, antecedent and consequent. *Antecedent concupiscence* is the sort which precedes an act of the will and is not willfully stimulated, such as sudden anger. *Consequent concupiscence* is that which is stimulated by the will, such as anger deliberately fostered.

MORAL PRINCIPLES CONCERNING CONCUPISCENCE. It is obvious

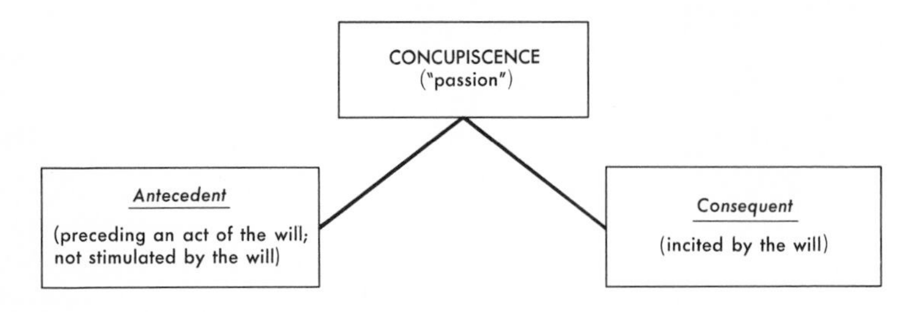

Figure 4. Types of concupiscence.

that certain emotions, such as anger, discouragement, or grief, can so influence a person's state of mind that the use of reason and free will is lessened. Antecedent concupiscence lessons the voluntary nature of human acts and lessens the degree of moral responsibility accordingly. On the other hand, consequent concupiscence does not lessen moral responsibility; rather, a person acting with consequent concupiscence is completely responsible. All will agree, for example, that a very depressed patient who attempts suicide is less blameworthy because he was in an emotional state (antecedent concupiscence). Again, people would hold fully responsible an employer who deliberately works himself into a fit of temper in order to impress a new employee (consequent concupiscence).

Violence

Violence is an external force applied by someone on another in order to compel him to perform an action against his will. In cases where the victim gives complete resistance, the violence is classified as perfect violence. However, if the victim offers insufficient resistance, the violence is classified as imperfect violence.

Perfect violence (that in which complete resistance is given) may be either physically or morally perfect. If a woman walking along a dark city street at night is attacked, and she attempts to fight off the attackers with all the physical powers at her command, she has been the victim of physically perfect violence. *Physically perfect violence is that in which every possible means of resisting*

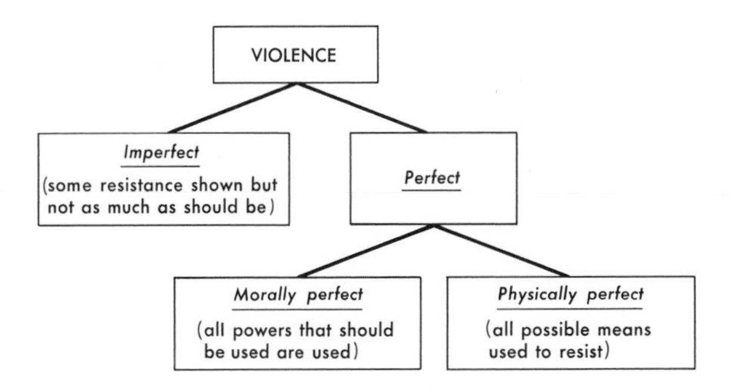

Figure 5. Types of violence.

is utilized. Now let us suppose that later the same night a man is walking down the same dangerous street and is accosted by robbers. At first he attempts to fight them off, but he soon realizes that any further resistance will probably result in his death, or at least in very severe beating, followed by the loss of his money anyway. Deciding that discretion is truly the better part of valor, he gives in, ceases to resist, and surrenders his money. Physically, he could resist further, but he is convinced that it would be useless. The violence of which he is victim is known as morally perfect violence. *Morally perfect violence is that in which all powers of resistance that should be used are employed.*

A different situation regarding violence exists in this case: A stenographer who is working after hours in an almost empty building is approached by the department head. The man, suddenly filled with lustful intentions, makes certain rough and violent advances. The young woman for a moment puts up some resistance and feels that additional resistance might terminate the incident. However, she quickly ceases resistance and gives in to the man. The stenographer is the victim of imperfect violence. *Imperfect violence is that in which some resistance is shown but not as much as should be.*

MORAL PRINCIPLES CONCERNING VIOLENCE. Regarding perfect violence, the moral principle is this: *That which is done from perfect violence is entirely involuntary, and so in such cases there is no moral responsibility.* If an individual is a victim in the absolute sense of the word, no sensible person will condemn him. If the victim makes a judgment that resistance is utterly useless, he need not resist. There is no obligation to do what is useless.

Regarding imperfect violence: *That which is done under the influence of imperfect violence is less voluntary, and so the moral responsibility is lessened* but not taken away completely. Suppose a captured soldier has been the subject of some brainwashing. Up to this point, it has not been severe, and he feels well able to take much more. Yet, in order to be allowed to go back to his cell and be left in peace, he reveals military secrets to the enemy. He has acted under imperfect violence. Another soldier is severely beaten by two spies, who then remove from his clothing certain secret papers he was carrying. This soldier is under the influence of perfect violence.

Other Factors Affecting the Voluntary Nature of Human Actions

Both popular realization and scientific studies recognize that freedom and full knowledge can be affected in individuals in various ways by such factors as habit, temperament, and mental states. A brief reference to the moral implication of these factors is in order.

Habit

A habit is an inclination to perform some particular action, acquired by repetition, and characterized by a decreased power of resistance and an increased facility of performance. It is also defined as "a stable quality superadded to a faculty positively inclining a person to act in a certain way."

A habit is sometimes called "second nature," meaning something deeply ingrained in an individual, but ingrained by being acquired rather than inborn. A habit is formed by repetition of an action. We are familiar with many habits in our daily life. Some have nothing to do with morality. Others have an intimate relation to moral behavior. The habit of cursing, of drinking, the habit of uncharitable speech, of lying—all have moral implications. *Habit does not destroy the voluntary nature of our acts.* A person is at least in some way responsible for acts done from habit as long as the habit is consciously allowed to endure. In performing some act through habit, that particular act may not be completely voluntary in itself, but it is at least voluntary in the sense that the habit was freely formed by the repetition of several previous acts. As long as we know the consequences of an act and do it repeatedly, we *will* that which follows.

Let us suppose that a woman has developed the habit of using God's name in vain constantly. She is now to the point that when people tell her of this, she does not even realize she has so spoken. At the present time she does not advert each time to what she says, but she has formed this habit by repeated voluntary and conscious language that should not have been used. She is responsible for the formation of the habit and must take appropriate steps to break it.

Temperament

Temperament is the sum total of those qualities which mark an individual. It is the sum total of native propensities which constitute an individual's disposition. Loosely, temperament may simply be defined as disposition.

Both heredity and environment play a part in forming a person's temperament. Psychologists list four major temperaments and their characteristics:

Sanguine—pleasing, agreeable, not a good leader because not very stable

Choleric—domineering, strong-willed, good leader

Melancholic—pessimistic, brooding, usually scrupulous, despairs easily

Phlegmatic—easy-going, lacking initiative, trustworthy

Of course, not every individual fits into this scheme in a clear-cut and inflexible manner. But it is easy to see that a person's native disposition can be a factor bearing on the voluntary nature of his acts.

MORAL IMPLICATIONS OF TEMPERAMENT. *A person's temperament can affect his will to the extent of somewhat lessening the completely voluntary nature of his actions.* This is rather evident. For instance, a person of extreme choleric disposition might be less guilty in certain circumstances when he loses his temper than an extremely phlegmatic type. A person in a mood of despair might be more affected by his temperament than by a conviction of mind arrived at through the use of reason. There was once a young woman who was very cold by nature—not at all passionate. She became a Communist, and in order to show her contempt for the bourgeois idea of God and His moral law, she deliberately engaged in illicit relations with one of the comrades for well over a year. Later she returned to her religion. Her cold nature was a factor adding to the gravity of her sins against purity, and she clearly realized this fact.

Nervous Mental Disorders

Nervous mental disorders can completely take away the voluntary nature of certain acts or can lessen the voluntary nature of those acts. A brief discussion of certain specific mental states will serve to indicate some of the moral implications involved.

Neurasthenia is a neurotic condition of debility characterized by feelings of fatigue, worry, and depression, which may affect the activity of the will. In some cases, the subject finds himself unable to make a decision or unable to act upon his decision. Loss of will power is technically known as *abulia.* Abulia may be complete or incomplete, according to the degree of loss of will power. It is to be noted that the loss of will power of which we speak is a true neurotic state, a pathological condition, as opposed to bad will or lack of moral stamina.

Hysteria is a psychoneurosis characterized by emotional excitability and frequently accompanied by various symptoms, many of which have moral implications. There are at times angry outbursts, a partial loss of memory, a tendency to lie or steal or to indulge in immoral conduct.

Compulsion neurosis is a psychoneurosis characterized by compulsions and obsessions. Included in this category are compulsive feelings and actions. Among these are various manias and phobias, such as pyromania (compulsive arson), kleptomania (compulsive stealing), claustrophobia (morbid dread of closed places), agoraphobia (morbid dread of open spaces), bacteriophobia (fear of germs), and pyrophobia (fear of fire). Here we note not only conditions in which the voluntary nature of acts is diminished or possibly precluded, but also conditions which may excuse from the fulfillment of a positive precept, such as claustrophobia excusing a Catholic from attendance at Mass on Sunday.

Melancholia is a mental disorder characterized by extreme depression and brooding. This pathological state should not be confused with a melancholy temperament, or with a temporary state of depression explainable in the light of actual circumstances. Melancholia may give rise to inability to pray or to fulfill other religious duties, and to a difficulty in making decisions or carrying them out. At times the patient may develop feelings of guilt which are unfounded.

Hypochondria is a morbid anxiety concerning one's own health, characterized by imaginary ailments. Extreme cases may at times be marked by a tendency to suicide.

MORAL IMPLICATIONS OF NERVOUS MENTAL DISORDERS. Sin and moral responsibility imply the use of the intellect and will. Nervous mental disorders at times affect the proper operation of these two faculties. To the extent to which these faculties are affected, moral responsibility is diminished or eliminated.

In concrete individual cases it is most difficult to determine moral responsibility. We must rest content to leave the final judgment in the hands of God. Caution should be exercised, however, lest there be any attempt to use a mental state as an unwarranted excuse for moral infractions. There is objectively a distinction between mental illness and moral turpitude. In some circles there is a tendency to so overemphasize the role of mental disorders as to virtually deny free will.

Cautions Regarding Moral Judgment

Placing a judgment upon the objective morality of a human act in the concrete involves a consideration of all the conditions which affect morality: the nature of the act itself, the purpose of the agent, circumstances, ignorance, fear, concupiscence, violence, habit, temperament, and nervous mental disorders. Judgment of the morality of a complicated case is no work for an amateur. Everyone has a conscience but everyone also has the duty of enlightening his conscience. At times this involves consultation with a person who has moral training. Caution is in order in judging morality. Even a highly trained and experienced moralist works with great care. It is certainly rash for a person untrained in moral science to make a quick judgment in an individual case, or to set himself up as an authority on moral matters. The wise layman holds the opinions of moral experts in great respect.

A particular caution must be given regarding the judging of one's own case. In this regard, great wisdom is expressed in the old saying, *Nemo judex in propria causa*—no one is a judge in his own case. When an important personal moral problem presents itself, it is time to seek competent advice.

Occasions of Sin

An occasion of sin is an extrinsic circumstance which offers a person an enticement to sin. The extrinsic circumstance may be a person (such as a bad companion), a place (as a notorious night club), or a thing (like an immoral book). An occasion of sin is sometimes defined as "any person, place, or thing which may lead us into sin."

Occasions of sin vary in intensity, and for that reason they are referred to as either *proximate* or *remote*. Proximate occasions are sometimes called "near occasions." *A proximate occasion of sin is one which may easily lead a person into sin.* Sometimes such occasions would tempt any normal person under normal circumstances, and in such cases the occasion is known as an *absolute* proximate occasion. For example, an obscene book is a temptation to all normal people, aside from some very extraordinary circumstances. On the other hand, some occasions of sin are such only for certain people, in which case they are called *relative* proximate occasions. A tavern is an occasion of sin to a drunkard, whereas to the average man it is not; therefore it is only a relative occasion.

A remote occasion of sin is one which is less likely to lead a person into sin. Here again we find a division into *absolute* and *relative.* An absolutely remote occasion of sin is that in which sin for an average person is possible but not probable, as for example reading the daily family newspaper. A relatively remote occasion of sin is that in which a particular individual or class of persons does not as a rule sin, although it does constitute a serious occasion for average people. Consider a book on human reproduction studied by a nurse, compared with the same book read by a curious teenager.

There is another division of occasions of sin, this one based on their necessity. Many occasions of sin are not at all necessary, such as going to a condemned motion picture for recreation. Such an occasion is classified as *free* or *voluntary*. But there are some occasions that cannot be avoided. It is physically impossible for a doctor to engage in general practice without entering some occasions of sin. A man may have a nagging wife who is the occasion of his losing his temper, but it is physically impossible to avoid her. Engaged couples sometimes find each other's company an occasion of sin, and although it is physically possible for them to avoid each other, it is morally impossible since it could be done only by grave inconvenience beyond what would be reasonably required. The doctor, the man with the nagging wife, the engaged couple are in *necessary* occasions of sin, occasions that cannot be avoided.

MORAL PRINCIPLES CONCERNING OCCASIONS OF SIN. We are morally obliged to avoid sin. Hence *we are obliged to avoid all voluntary*

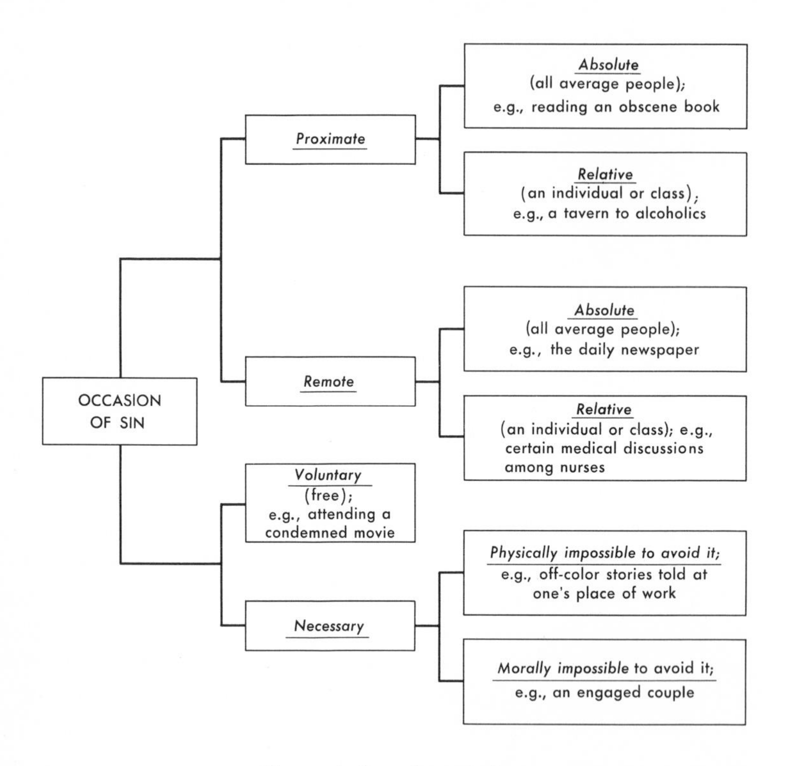

Figure 6. Occasions of sin.

proximate occasions of sin, unless we have a sufficient reason. If a person finds himself in a necessary proximate occasion, he should take steps to render it remote. In the case of the man with the nagging wife, he should exercise strong will power to avoid losing his temper, pray for God's special help, give his wife a good example by his own good life, avoid as best he can those things that occasion her nagging, encourage her to practice her religion faithfully, and in short take every practical step to minimize the occasion of sin. It is well to remember that when a person is in a necessary occasion of sin, God will give him special spiritual help to avoid the sin, whereas if he voluntarily enters the occasion, he deserves no special help. "Danger loved is death won."

We have a light obligation to avoid remote occasions of sin unless we have a sufficient reason; but the reason need only be light, and there is generally a sufficient reason. In such cases there is only a slight danger of sinning, and the temptation can easily be resisted. A man is morally allowed to continue his custom of reading the daily family newspaper, although from time to time it may offer a slight temptation. Actually we could not go through life avoiding all remote occasions of sin. Any attempt to do so would throw us into a state of scrupulosity, which is an unhealthy condition.

May God grant us the light to know what is right, the strength to do it, the wisdom to avoid occasions of sin, and the charity to give good example always.

Topics for Discussion

Items may be true, partly true, erroneous, or unsolvable. First judge, then discuss.

1. In this chapter ignorance, fear, violence, concupiscence, habit, temperament, and mental disorders were discussed as factors affecting the voluntary nature of human acts and consequently eliminating or lessening moral responsibility. Are there other factors that might also be discussed in this connection?
2. If a nurse has absorbed all the knowledge imparted to her during her time of training, then any knowledge she does not have can be excused as being invincible ignorance.
3. It is not just to inflict punishment if a person's free will is hampered, as for instance when he is an alcoholic or a drug addict.

Cases for Solution

1. A nurse is told by the hospital administrator to omit a blood transfusion ordered by the doctor because the patient is going to die eventually anyway and is so sick that he will not know the difference.

The hospital in this way will make some needed money, since the family can be charged for the blood. The nurse knows that this is wrong, but fears that she will lose her job if she does not cooperate. She obeys the orders of the administrator.

2. A student working in the operating room of a small hospital where the moral and ethical standards are high finds out that the next morning she is to scrub in on a bilateral salpingectomy. She has heard that this might involve a question of morality and so asks one of her friends who is a charge nurse on one of the floors. Her friend tells her that she has nothing to worry about. She assists at the operation.
3. A senior student working on one of the floors suspects that a recently hired cleaner is taking petty change from patients when they are too sick to know of it. She says to herself, "What you don't know won't hurt you," and fearing a "scene" if she brings the matter to the attention of the charge nurse, she decides not to investigate the matter further but to let her suspicion remain just that.
4. A student nurse is slightly tempted to evil thoughts by some of the reading she is required to do in pursuit of her studies. Must she discontinue her studies and resign from the school?
5. A student is found reading an obscene magazine in the presence of several others in the recreation room. On the grounds that she has given grave scandal to her fellow students, she is dismissed from the school. Are the authorities justified in this action?

References for Further Study

Bourke, V. J. *Ethics: A Textbook in Moral Philosophy*, New York: The Macmillan Company, 1953.

Davis, H. *Moral and Pastoral Theology*, London: Sheed and Ward, Ltd., 1945.

Finney, Patrick, and O'Brien, Patrick. *Moral Problems in Hospital Practice*, St. Louis: B. Herder Book Co., 1956.

Ford, J. C., and Kelly, G. *Contemporary Moral Theology*, Westminster, Md.: The Newman Press, 1960, Vol. I.

Healy, E. F. *Moral Guidance*, Chicago: Loyola University Press, 1960.

Jone, H., and Adelman, U. *Moral Theology*, Westminster, Md.: The Newman Press, 1952.

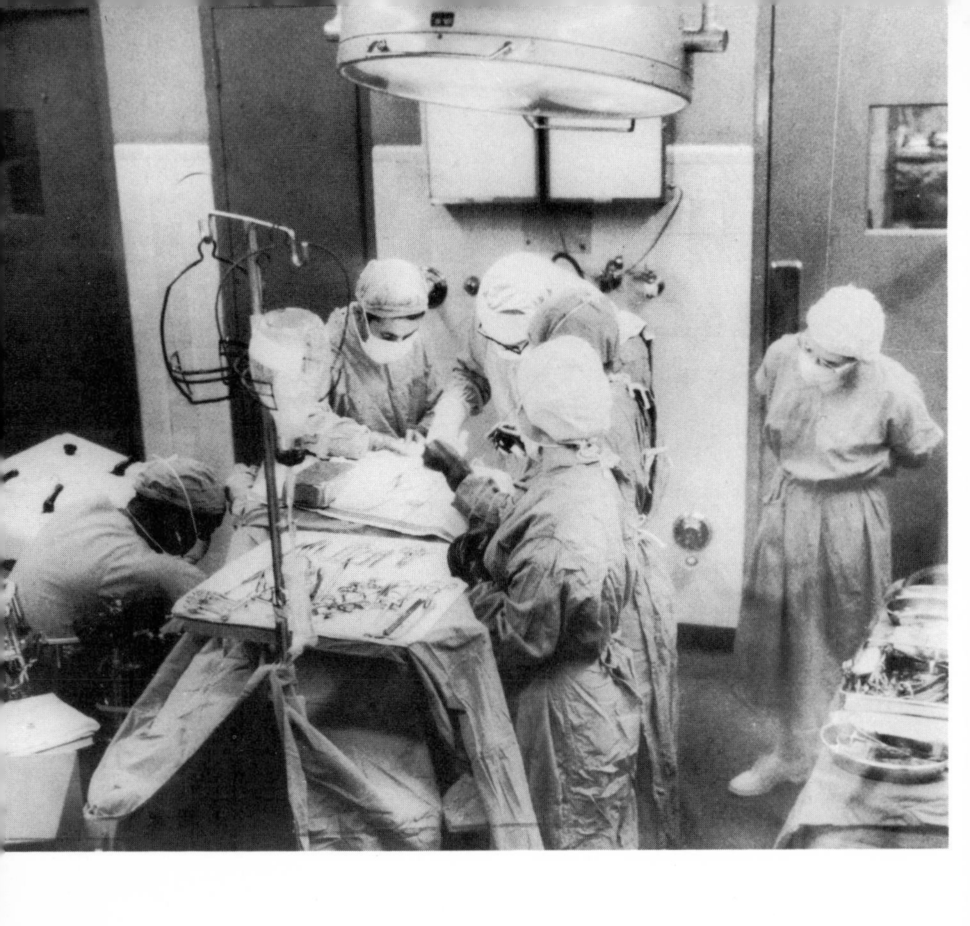

Newark Beth Israel Hospital, Newark, New Jersey.

CHAPTER 3

Law and Conscience

Natural law · Positive law · Conscience

Natural Law

The natural law is the code of moral conduct which reason indicates as conformable to human nature. For example, man is by nature adapted to live in society, and consequently those actions are good which are conformable to the welfare of society, such as telling the truth, obeying lawful authority, paying one's debts; whereas those actions are bad which will tend to disrupt society, such as stealing or rebelling against lawful authority. Again, man is by nature a rational being with a spiritual soul which should keep the desires of the body in proper check. Hence it is morally good by the natural law to be temperate and chaste, whereas it is opposed to the natural law to drink to excess or to seek sexual gratification inordinately. Further, man as a creature of God owes to his Creator certain duties, such as worship.

Properties of the Natural Law

The natural law exists in its subjects by reason of the fact that it is an integral part of their very nature. Just as the laws of chemical reaction are inherent in the nature of the elements, so certain moral laws are inherent in the nature of man. A young child who has done wrong—lied, stolen, or the like—feels uncomfortable, ashamed, or frightened, though he has never heard of the moral law. His reason indicates that some things are wrong by their very nature. We say that such things are against the natural law.

If everyone, for example, could take the property of others at any time without fault or blame, no one would have any security in the possession of his property. All effort, all planning would be useless. Initiative would be stifled. The entire world would be in chaos. In other words, reason indicates that stealing is wrong. Therefore we say that stealing is against the natural law. The same can be said for murder, adultery, rape, lying, and a host of other evils.

Natural law is *universal* because, being based on human nature, it binds all men. It is *immutable* because human nature is the same at all times and in all places. Therefore all acts contrary to the natural law, such as murder, theft, voluntary direct abortion, and birth control, will always remain immoral. *No human authority has the power to dispense, alter, or abrogate any precept of the natural law.*

The Ten Commandments

The Ten Commandments are basically a summary of the principles of the natural law. The only exception to this is the Third Commandment, "Remember to keep the Sabbath day holy," which is a divine positive law. Men, even before the Ten Commandments were given, could tell right from wrong. But men drifted away from God, and He saw the need of putting His law before them in a striking way, making it stronger and more explicit than the natural law they already knew.

The entire natural law is not listed in detail in the Ten Commandments. They list the violations of natural law. For example, "Honor thy father and thy mother" embraces by implication all the obligations incumbent upon superiors and inferiors in their relations with each other. The Commandments make no pretense at being an exhaustive list of every possible infringement of natural laws. They are a series of important guideposts indicating the proper line of conduct in various important departments of life.

In the course of human history, we find practically no argument over the authority of the Ten Commandments. They are so obviously expressive of the law of our nature that few have been so bold and illogical as to challenge them.

Classification of Precepts of the Natural Law

Precepts embodied in the natural law are classified as universal principles, immediate conclusions, and remote conclusions.

Universal principles of the natural law are those which are so fundamental that they are *known by all men.* They are self-evident. For example, it is evident to all that good is to be done and evil is to be avoided.

Immediate conclusions of the natural law are those which are *known by all men apart from very extraordinary cases* where culture and religious training are lacking; for example, God must be worshiped, parents should be honored.

Remote conclusions are those which are *deduced* from the primary principles by means of practical reasoning and which may be inadequately grasped by many. For example, the obligation of restoring to the owner an object which has been found.

The Natural Law and Happiness

The natural law is not meant to interfere with our liberty but to guide us in the proper use of our freedom. A railing is placed on the side of a narrow path along a precipice not to hinder the people who walk along but to protect them. They are free to step under or over the railing, but in doing so they only endanger themselves. Man cannot ignore the law of nature without doing himself harm. The Ten Commandments are a set of God's directions on how human beings can avoid harm to themselves and attain happiness both in this life and in the life to come.

Positive Law

A positive law is a precept imposed by one in authority. In some instances this authority may be God, as in the many ceremonial laws of the Old Testament or the necessity of baptism stated in the New

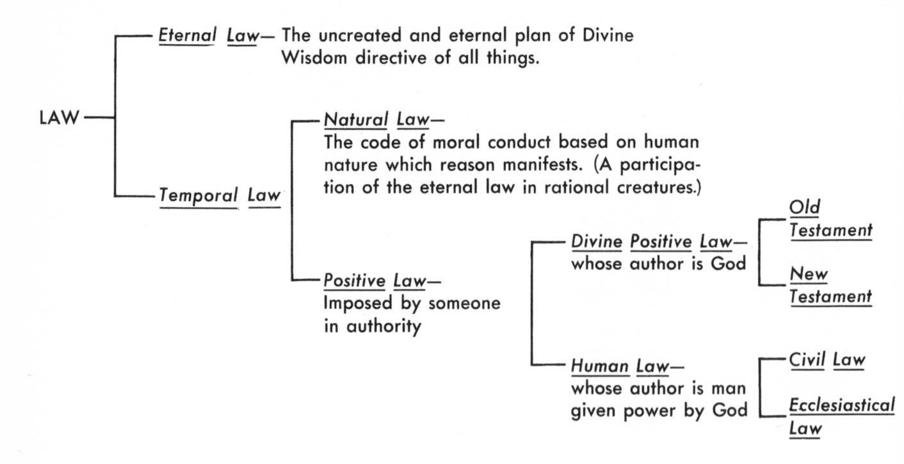

Figure 7. Sources of our moral guidance.

Testament. When God is the author of a positive law, it is called "divine positive law." In other instances the authority is human, as in the case of taxes and the formalities of a will in civil law, or the obligations of Sunday Mass or Friday abstinence in ecclesiastical law. This sort of law is called "human law." Positive laws, being made by authority, can be changed or abrogated by that same authority.

Conscience

Conscience is a judgment of human reason concerning the moral goodness or evil of one's own action.

Conscience is not a separate faculty, a special little voice within us, whispering suggestions regarding our conduct. It is an act of the human intellect regarding an action with respect to moral matters. It is a practical judgment of the intellect as to what is right or wrong.

Types of Conscience

Conscience, being an operation of the human intellect, is subject to the shortcomings of such an intellect. In addition, the operation of conscience implies knowledge, freedom, and reflection. These are variables, and in the light of such variables it is easy to see that a different judgment may be made by different individuals concerning the morality of the same act. Keeping those factors in mind, we may enumerate and explain various types of conscience.

In this discussion, we are concerned only with what is called antecedent conscience, which is a judgment made previous to an act. We are not talking here of consequent conscience, which is a judgment made after an act, such as that in preparation for confession.

True and False Conscience

From the viewpoint of the relationship of conscience to objective truth, conscience may be either *true* or *erroneous.*

A true conscience is one which indicates correctly the goodness or badness of moral conduct.

An erroneous conscience (sometimes called a false conscience) *is one which falsely indicates that a good action is evil or an evil action is good.* Since conscience is nothing more than the operation of the intellect in a particular field, it is apparent that conscience may be in error. Everyone knows that the human intellect is capable of error. The fact that the intellect is operating in the field of morality or the fact that we give it a special name and call it "conscience" does not confer infallibility. An error of conscience may at times exist because of some fault on the part of the individual, but we are here discussing an inculpably erroneous conscience. Suppose an orderly finds out that a patient has made some uncharitable remarks about him and feels justified in making slanderous remarks in return. Such slanderous remarks are not, in fact, justified. Therefore the orderly is acting with an erroneous conscience.

Moral Implications of an Inculpably False Conscience

If a person performs an act that is objectively a light sin, when his conscience tells him it is a serious sin, he has committed a serious sin. A boy who thinks that it is a mortal sin to steal a small amount of money, and yet deliberately does so, is guilty of a mortal sin.

If a person commits what is objectively a serious sin, truly thinking it is a light offense, he is guilty only of a light offense. A small boy, although realizing that it is wrong to strike his mother, thinks that it is not seriously wrong. His conscience is in error. Although the act was objectively a serious sin, he is only guilty of a slight sin.

We may even go further regarding false conscience. If a person performs an action that is not evil, but his conscience tells him it is evil, he is guilty of a wrong. A man who thinks the use of slang is a sin, as a result of his error of conscience, has sinned by using it. However, we must remember that no one can commit a sin when circumstances force him to act in a particular way. A Catholic patient who has been told by his doctor that he has pneumonia and must remain in bed on Sunday commits no sin by missing Mass, no matter what his confused conscience may tell him. No one is held to do the impossible.

Certain and Doubtful Conscience

A certain conscience is one which dictates a course of action in clear terms without fear of error. It clearly labels as good or bad an action contemplated. A man tempted to seek revenge by committing a murder can clearly see that he is contemplating the performance of a gravely evil act.

A doubtful conscience is one which leaves a person undecided as to the proper course of action. A Catholic, forgetting that it is Friday, stops at a restaurant and orders a turkey dinner. Just as he begins to eat the turkey, he remembers what day it is. On the one hand, he has a problem concerning Church law. On the other hand, he has a problem concerning his stomach, his pocketbook, and his public embarrassment. Unable to arrive at a satisfactory decision, he is a victim of a doubtful conscience.

Lax, Scrupulous, and Tender Conscience

LAX CONSCIENCE. Conscience may err on the side of laxity. Those with a lax conscience sometimes become persuaded that great sins are permissible. They find excuses for grave misconduct. Such people often begin by rationalizing minor faults, until their conscience becomes dull and incapable of proper direction. Example of lax conscience: A nurse reveals a very serious professional secret to lay people and considers the disclosure mere small talk.

SCRUPULOUS CONSCIENCE. Rarer than laxity of conscience is scrupulosity. The person with a scrupulous conscience sees evil where there is none. Saint Francis de Sales points out that scrupulosity has its source in pride. Let no one think that a scrupulous conscience is to be admired. Scruples are a definite evil, and a tremendous drag upon the soul—as much to be avoided as laxity. Example of scrupulous conscience: A nurse engages in hospital small talk with another nurse and then feels guilty of a grave violation of professional secrecy.

TENDER CONSCIENCE. A conscience which forms a correct judgment with comparative facility even in matters which involve a fine distinction is called a tender conscience. It is also sometimes called a "delicate conscience." Such a conscience is developed by many sincere people. In achieving this desirable goal, the guidance of a regular confessor or spiritual director is of tremendous value.

Obligations Relative to Conscience

When our conscience is honestly and correctly formed, we are obliged to follow it in any circumstances. Once we are convinced that we have an obligation to do or avoid a certain action, we are duty bound to act upon our convictions.

No institution and no person, no church, no pope can claim dominion over conscience. Amongst all inalienable rights, the rights of conscience come first. . . . Beyond priest, preacher, prophet; beyond the

Bible and the Church, a man may appeal to conscience. We may even make bold to say that in a certain sense, a man may appeal from God to conscience. God may speak, God may thunder. But if a man does not hear, or hearing does not understand, he will still be saved if he follows his conscience.[1]

With this general norm in mind, we may give the following specific rules of conduct.

An individual must always act in accordance with a certain conscience. This is true even if the certain conscience is false. If one's conscience points out a particular action as definitely bad, even though objectively that act is good, the act must be avoided. Conversely, if the conscience of an individual points out an act as good and to be done, even though objectively the act is evil, that individual must perform the act.

No one is allowed to act with a doubtful conscience. The obligation in such circumstances is to resolve the doubt. If, then, a hospital employee were to say: "I am not sure whether to take this would be stealing or not, so I'll take the benefit of the doubt and go ahead," he would be acting wrongly. An individual should be morally certain that a particular action is permissible before performing it.

Norms for Resolving a Doubtful Conscience

If one is in doubt whether there is a law forbidding a particular action, or whether his action would be in these particular circumstances forbidden by the law, *he should obtain advice* if possible. At times it is not possible to obtain expert advice at the moment. In such cases, a person may utilize some general moral norms for resolving a doubtful conscience.

One basic moral norm that may be followed can be stated in the following way: *If a person is in doubt concerning the lawfulness*

[1] Rev. James A. Gillis, *So Near Is God*, New York: Charles Scribner's Sons, 1953, p. 63. London: Burns & Oates, Ltd. Used with permission.

of an action, he may follow an opinion that is well founded, at least if it is as probable as the opposite.

A person may follow this principle in a doubt concerning any law, human or divine, positive or natural.

A well-founded opinion implies a belief that a fact is so, but with the realization that there is a possibility (even a probability) that the opposite may be true. We may, for instance, be of the opinion that a republic is the most efficient form of government but realize that some other form might be better. The opinion is well founded which is based upon reasons that are weighty enough to convince a prudent person, even though he may still realize that the opposite opinion could be the true one.

If a well-founded opinion is based upon the authority of a person other than ourselves, it is said to be based upon *extrinsic* reasons. If I believe that medication A is the best treatment for disease B because a most eminent specialist on disease B is of that opinion, then my well-founded opinion is based on extrinsic reasons. Or, to put it more directly, it is based on authority.

If a well-founded opinion is based upon my personal analysis and judgment of the facts—presuming that I am competent and impartial—then my opinion is said to be based upon *intrinsic* reasons. If I believe that a certain medication is best because as a doctor I have made a thorough study of the matter and reached that conclusion, then the reasons for my opinion are intrinsic.

We are never allowed to follow even a more probable opinion when to do so might cause bodily or spiritual harm to ourselves or another. *To avoid physical or spiritual damage, the safer course must be followed.* Theologians may put forth various opinions as to the validity of baptism when liquids other than water are used, but their opinions will have to remain in the realm of theory. In actual practice, it is our serious obligation to take the safer course in the use of matter for baptism. In a case of doubt regarding medication, the safer course must always be followed. A nurse feels that most probably this is the proper medicine, but it might be poison; she may not administer it.

Decision of Conscience is Final

Conscience is the umpire who "calls the play" in our moral life, and the decision of conscience is final. There is no appeal above conscience. Furthermore, enlightenment of conscience at a later date has no retroactive effect; it does not change the morality of an act performed in the past when conscience was in error. As some people grow older, they begin to worry about their sins as children. They know now that some things they did were objectively very wrong, although to their young minds they did not seem serious at the time. To allow one's conscience to be thus concerned is a futile pursuit. God will not judge us in the light of knowledge acquired later. The subjective morality of our past acts has been determined forever. A newly enlightened conscience affects not the past but the future.

Topics for Discussion

Items may be true, partly true, erroneous, or unsolvable. First judge, then discuss.

1. Conscience is an infallible guide in each individual. If we act according to our conscience we are acting rightly whether or not we have received training in ethics. Therefore good will and sincerity for a nurse are more important than a thorough knowledge of moral principles.
2. The natural law is the code of moral conduct which reason indicates as conformable to human nature. This, then, should apply in the same way to all people regardless of religious convictions. Yet a considerable number of people believe that the Catholic Church is particularly strict on many things.
3. All men do not agree on the so-called principles of the natural law. This proves that they are not universal principles.

Cases for Solution

1. A nurse says that her conscience clearly dictates that she should not assist at a particular operation. One of the doctors present says that

he went to a Catholic medical school and he would assure her that the operation is not immoral. Should the nurse follow her conscience or the advice of the doctor?

2. "Most priests do not understand medical terminology and medical problems," is the remark of a nurse. "As long as I am not certain that anything I do is morally wrong, then I go ahead and do it." Is she acting correctly?

References for Further Study

Davis, H. *Moral and Pastoral Theology,* London: Sheed and Ward, Ltd., 1945, 4 vol.

Farrell, W. *A Companion to the Summa,* New York: Sheed and Ward, Ltd., 1952.

Finney, Patrick, and O'Brien, Patrick. *Moral Problems in Hospital Practice,* St. Louis: B. Herder Book Co., 1956.

Healy, E. F. *Moral Guidance,* Chicago: Loyola University Press, 1960.

Jone, H. and Adelman, U. *Moral Theology,* Westminster, Md.: The Newman Press, 1953.

Marshall, John. *The Ethics of Medical Practice,* London: Darton, Longman & Todd, 1960.

(RELIGIOUS NEWS SERVICE PHOTO.)

Pius XII, Pope of Medicine.

CHAPTER 4

The Twofold Effect

IN OUR EVERYDAY LIFE, we frequently perform actions which have more than one effect. For example, a family supports a Catholic school. On the one hand this results in a financial burden; on the other there are the benefits of a religious education for their children.

Some actions have two good effects, such as going to church, which gives glory to God and good example to our neighbor. Some actions have two bad effects, such as drunkenness, which deprives the drinker of his use of reason and gives scandal to others.

Obviously, all acts that have only morally good effects may be done, and acts which have only morally evil effects may not be done. However, if an action has both a good and a bad effect, we are confronted with a problem as to whether or not the action may be performed.

Important Distinctions

Before explaining the principle of the twofold effect, some important distinctions should be pointed out. When we perform various actions, they are followed by various effects, some of which we desire (wish, intend, want, will), others of which we do not desire but merely allow (permit, tolerate). A fireman enters a burning building; he wills to extinguish the fire; he tolerates inhaling quantities of smoke. A woman goes to a beautician; she wills to have her hair set according to the latest style; she tolerates sitting under the heat for a period of time. A girl's features are marred by a large, ugly nose; she undergoes an operation; she wills the correction of an abnormality; she tolerates several uncomfortable days in the hospital.

Sin is an act of the will. Since this is so, obviously the distinction between what is willed or intended and what is tolerated or merely permitted enters at times into moral judgment.

Another distinction must be kept in mind when dealing with the principle of the twofold effect. There is a difference between performing a good act which has both good and evil effects and performing an evil act in order that good may result. If the officials of a state decree that a necessary new highway shall be built, they perform an act that benefits the common good, while at the same time working some hardship upon those individuals who are required to move away to make room for the highway. Both the good and the evil come from the good law. But if the government decrees that all insane people shall be killed in order to decrease taxes, the good effect results from the evil. The government performs an evil act: murder. Following from this, as a link in a chain, there are lower taxes. The lowering of taxes is an effect of an effect. It only occurs by reason of the fact that thousands of people are murdered. Sterilizing a woman so that she cannot add additional members to her financially overburdened family is another example of achieving a good purpose by an evil act; the benefit comes by reason of an immoral procedure. There is the important distinction. There is a moral difference between the performance of a good act that has some good and some bad effects and the performance of an evil act that will result in some good.

Four Conditions

Under the principle of the twofold effect, the science of ethics lays down certain conditions which must be fulfilled to justify an action that has both a good and a bad effect. These conditions are the following:

1. The action must be in itself morally good or at least morally indifferent.
2. The good effect of the action must not come from an evil effect but must come from the action itself directly.
3. The good must be willed, and the evil merely allowed.
4. The good effect must be at least equivalent in importance to the evil effect. In other words, there must be sufficient reason to permit the evil effect.

Although these rules may sound complicated, in actuality all people apply them frequently. A little boy cuts his hand. His mother applies iodine to the injury. This action has two effects: it gives the boy pain and it wards off infection. Although she did not realize it, she actually applied the four principles that we have listed. She performed an action which is in itself good, namely, putting antiseptic on the boy's hand. The good effect did not come from the pain but rather occurred from the use of the iodine. The mother certainly did not will to give her child pain but only desired to help him. Finally, the good effect of warding off infection is far greater than the evil effect of the slight sting of the antiseptic.

When we are confronted with more serious problems, it is important that a proper application of the principle of twofold effect be made, in order that great moral evil may be avoided.

The classic example is one that involves the right to life. It is the case of a woman in a nonviable stage of pregnancy, with cancer of the uterus, when immediate hysterectomy is indicated to save her life. This procedure, of course, would result in the death of the fetus. The surgery will produce two effects: the good effect is the saving of the life of the mother; the bad effect is the death of the offspring. This operation is morally permissible by reason of the principle of the twofold effect, and of course a nurse may assist.

First of all, the action of removing a cancerous organ is in itself morally good. Second, the good effect is a direct result of the action, and not a result of the death of the fetus. Third, the intention of the doctor and the nurse is to save the life of the mother, not to murder the child. And finally, the saving of the mother's life is in proportion to the death of the fetus.

When the Principle Does Not Apply

Now let us turn to a case which would not fall under this principle. Hyperemesis gravidarum (pernicious vomiting) is easily solved by the termination of the pregnancy. However, this is not morally permissible. It violates the rules of the twofold effect in the following ways:

1. The action is not morally good or even indifferent; it is evil. It is a direct attack upon an innocent life.

2. The good effect, namely, the health of the mother, follows from the evil. It is because the child has been killed that the mother is cured. In short, termination of pregnancy in the case of hyperemesis gravidarum is not morally permissible because the end never justifies the means. We may not do evil in order that good may come of it.

Applying the Twofold Effect

Case 1. A commanding officer orders the bombing of a military base. He is aware that there are civilians on the base and civilian families living nearby, some of whom will probably be killed. Is the commanding officer acting morally? By checking each of the four conditions of the twofold effect, we see that he is. Bombing of a legitimate military target is not an evil act; the good effect (hastening the end of the war) does not come about through the evil effect (death of civilians); the commander wills only the destruction of the military objective, not the death of the civilians. The defense of one's country against an unjust aggressor (a just war) constitutes a sufficient reason for the bombing if the number killed is not too great.

Case 2. A married woman complains of pain, and upon examination the doctor discovers that an abnormal pregnancy has occurred. The implantation has taken place in the fallopian tube instead of the uterus (ectopic gestation). If he does nothing, the tube will swell further and finally rupture, probably killing the

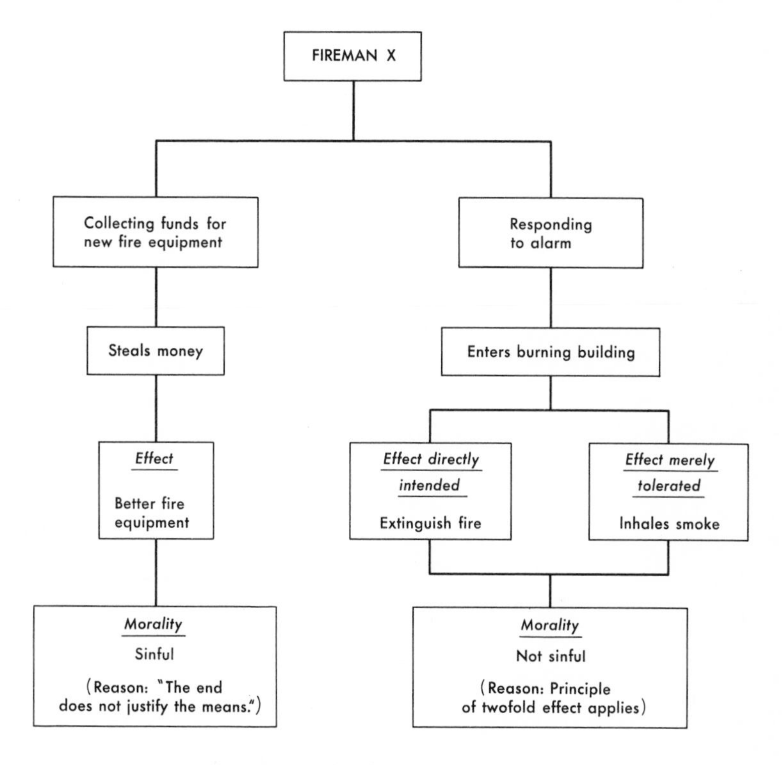

Figure 8A. The twofold effect.

woman. The only cure is to remove the tube promptly, which will save the mother and result in the death of the fetus. Is it moral for the doctor to operate? Yes, it is. The tube being in a pathologic condition, it is moral to remove it, under the principle of the twofold effect. The purpose of the procedure is to remove a pathologic organ which is a threat to the life of the mother. The death of the fetus is unintended and merely tolerated.

Case 3. The leader of a nation engaged in war orders the execu-

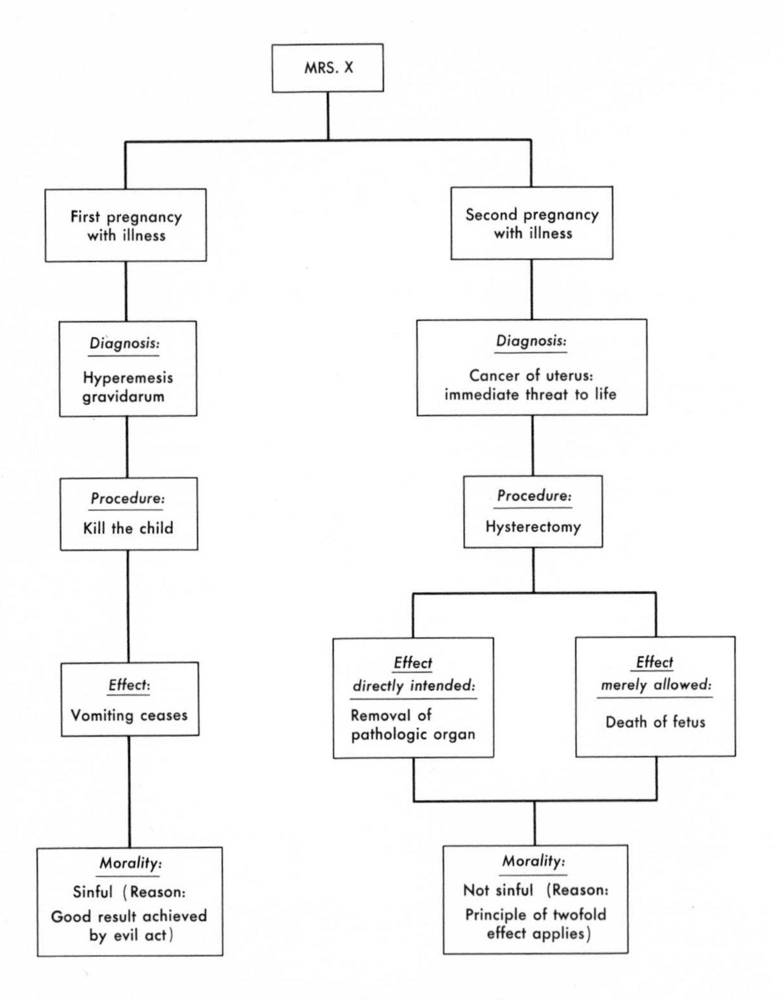

Figure 8B. The twofold effect.

tion of all inmates of mental institutions and old-age homes, in order to devote full manpower and resources to the quicker termination of the war. Is this order morally justified? In spite of the stated good intention, it is not. This action (killing of innocent civilians) is murder, which is intrinsically evil; the good effect would come about through the evil effect, the evil is not merely tolerated but is intended.

The principle of the twofold effect finds frequent and wide application in modern medicine. In most cases the solution is very obvious. However, occasionally very difficult cases may arise. In such situations a person specially trained in moral matters should be consulted.

Topics for Discussion

Items may be true, partly true, erroneous, or unsolvable. First judge, then discuss.

1. What right does the Church have to make an arbitrary formula such as the twofold effect for solving moral difficulties?
2. There is an old saying worthy of consideration: "Better to lie a little than be unhappy much." What is the relationship between this proverb and the principle of the twofold effect?
3. Is boxing morally justified? Football? Discuss how the four conditions necessary for application of the twofold-effect principle would apply to each of these sports.

Cases for Solution

1. A nurse on her way to the hospital to go on duty at 11 P.M. is passing through a dark street where a considerable number of assaults have been reported. She is attacked from behind. Not knowing what is in the mind of the attacker, she stabs him in the heart.
2. A doctor in the armed services in an outlying district of the tropics comes across a native with spinal meningitis. He has no instruments or means of sterilization. He feels that if he treats the native, he will contract the disease. He also feels responsible for 150 soldiers who need his medical help and may die without him.
3. A crewman aboard a burning oil tanker, realizing that an explosion is imminent, jumps into the sea, although he is unable to swim.
4. A chaplain stays in the burning wing of a hospital to administer the last rites. He can escape if he leaves now. If he stays, he will certainly be trapped and killed.
5. A pregnant woman has untreated syphilis. She is told by a doctor that medical research has discovered that her child will also have syphilis. In order to prevent the suffering and blighted life that the child would have to endure if it were born, she arranges for an abortion.
6. The commanding officer of an army orders the bombing of a small

town in the territory of an enemy nation. By this means he hopes to so demoralize the enemies that the war will be soon terminated and in this way thousands of lives will be saved on both sides. Is his action justified?

7. The captain of a sunken fishing boat which had 60 persons on board has managed to rescue 15 in a lifeboat. Thirty-five others have life jackets on and will probably be picked up in time. The lifeboat is already overloaded and will probably capsize if any others are taken aboard, and so the captain hastens to row away from the scene of the accident lest those already in the lifeboat also perish.
8. A military pilot willingly obeys an order to crash a plane loaded with bombs into an aircraft carrier of the enemy. He knows that he will be killed, but the bombs will destroy the ship.
9. A doctor has just delivered a hydrocephalic with multiple anomalies. He knows that to administer any lethal drug and immediately kill the baby would be wrong, and so instead he simply orders that no medical aid should be given. Since nothing positive is done to kill the child, but only a refraining from positive action, the doctor feels that for the sake of the mother and the child this is justified.
10. A special agent has been assigned to guard the life of an important national dignitary visiting a large city. A fanatic attempts to take the life of the dignitary by shooting him. The agent, in order to protect his charge, steps in front of him and is shot. Is he justified in so sacrificing his life?

References for Further Study

Healy, E. F. *Moral Guidance,* Chicago: Loyola University Press, 1960.

Kenny, John P. *Principles of Medical Ethics,* Westminster, Md.: The Newman Press, 1962.

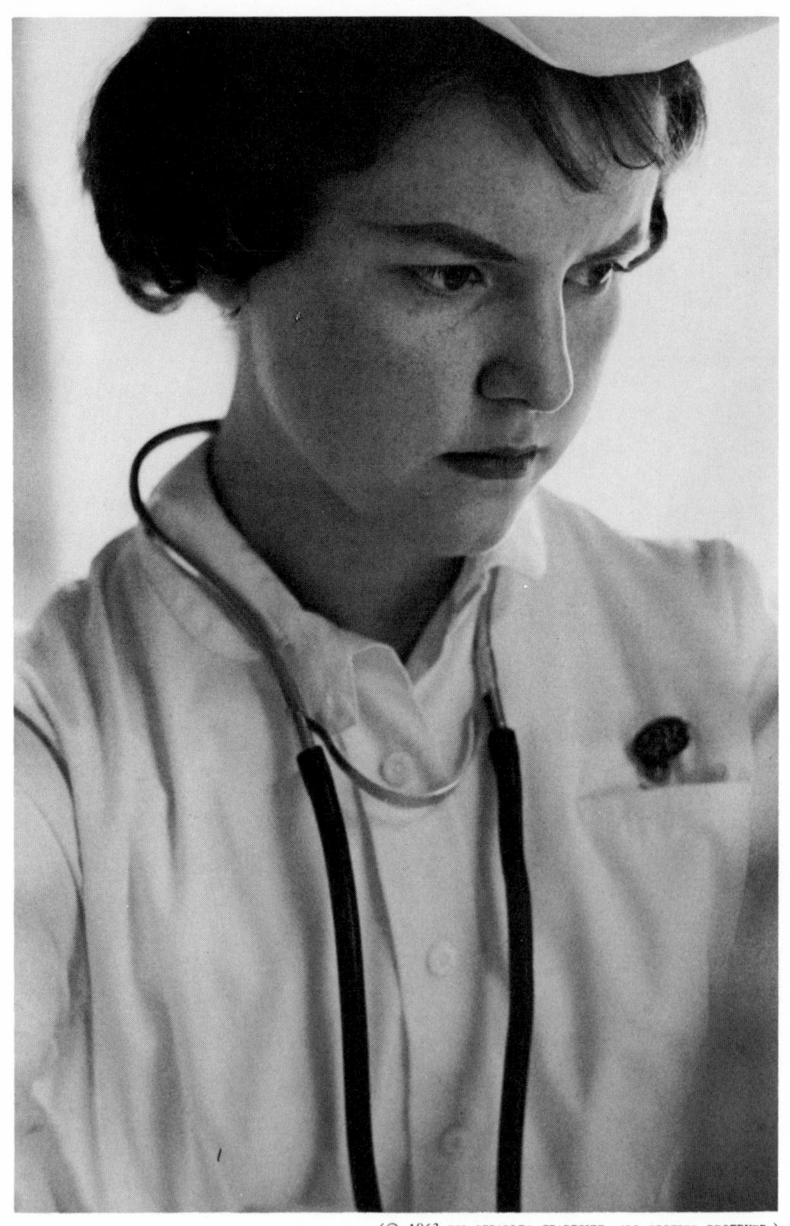

St. Vincent's Hospital, New York.

CHAPTER 5

Moral Guides and Maxims

The rule of ordinary means · The principle of subsidiarity · The principle of totality · Epikia · Moral maxims

IN OUR DAILY LIFE we have proverbs by which we bring out a truth in order to guide our lives. The short phrases: "Beggars can't be choosers," "Clothes do not make the man," "A man is known by the company he keeps"—all are generalizations in a popular vein which contain a bit of wisdom or truth by which to guide our actions. In a similar way, there are many moral guides and maxims which, if rightly understood, can be a help to interpreting the moral law. We shall discuss several of these, giving an interpretation and some examples as to how they can be applied. In many cases a concise Latin phrase sums up the maxim. For those for whom the Latin phrases may prove meaningful, we include these phrases.

It is to be noted that a brief list of this kind by no means constitutes a complete treatment of moral principles. Such a treatment can be given only in a course in moral theology. We merely give these maxims to introduce the student to some general moral principles and to aid in the development of moral judgment.

The Rule of Ordinary Means

"Natural reason and [principles of] Christian morality say that man (and whoever is entrusted with the task of taking care of his fellowman) has the right and the duty in case of serious illness to take the necessary means for the preservation of life and health. Normally one is held only to use ordinary means—according to circumstances of persons, places, times, and culture—that is to say, means that do not involve any unusually grave burden for oneself or another."[1] Some medical means are clearly ordinary, others clearly extraordinary. For example, a blood transfusion in most circumstances today would be an ordinary means, whereas the amputation of two legs is extraordinary. However, there are various medical procedures in which there must be a thoughtful weighing of circumstances in order to determine in individual cases just what would be an extraordinary means. Certainly the medical profession as well as the public in general wishes to take every means possible and spare no effort to preserve life and health. This is commendable and this is their *right.* But we should remember that normally speaking, there is no *obligation* to utilize extraordinary means.

An example of the application of this moral norm may be cited in the words of Pope Pius XII. Speaking to anesthetists, he indicated how the principle of ordinary means applies to the prolongation of life by artificial respiration:

> Does the anesthetist have the right, or is he bound, in all cases of deep unconsciousness, even in those that are considered to be completely hopeless in the opinion of a competent doctor, to use modern artificial respiration apparatus, even against the will of the family?
>
> In ordinary cases one will grant that the anesthetist has the right to act in this manner, but he is not bound to do so, unless this becomes the only way of fulfilling another certain moral duty.
>
> The rights and duties of the doctor are correlative to those of the patient. The doctor, in fact, has no separate or independent right where the patient is concerned. In general he can take action only if the patient explicitly or implicitly, directly or indirectly, gives him permission.
>
> The procedure of resuscitation which concerns us here does not contain anything immoral in itself. Therefore, the patient if he were capable of making a personal decision could lawfully use it and, consequently, give the doctor permission to use it.

[1] Pope Pius XII, Address to delegates to the International Congress of Anesthetists in Rome. November 24, 1957. This pope has been called "The Pope of Medicine" because he is the author of over 90 documents pertaining to medicine and nursing.

On the other hand, since these forms of treatment go beyond the ordinary means to which one is bound, it cannot be held that there is an obligation to use them nor, consequently, that one is bound to give the doctor permission to use them.

The rights and duties of the family generally depend upon the presumed will of the unconscious patient, if he is of age and "sui juris." Where the proper and independent duty of the family is concerned, they are usually bound only to the use of ordinary means.

Consequently, if it appears that the attempt at resuscitation constitutes in reality such a burden for the family that one cannot in all conscience impose it upon them, they can lawfully insist that the doctor should discontinue these attempts and the doctor can lawfully comply.

There is not involved here a case of direct disposal of the life of the patient, nor of euthanasia in any way, which would never be licit.

Even when it causes the arrest of circulation, the interruption of attempts at resuscitation is never more than an indirect cause of the cessation of life, and one must apply in this case the principle of the twofold effect.[2]

To preserve life we must take ordinary means, but usually we need not take extraordinary means. Some things are quite clearly in most circumstances ordinary, such as the taking of some medicine, or a minor operation on one's foot. Others are quite clearly extraordinary means, e.g., the amputation of two legs. A person would not be obliged to undergo a serious operation for cancer of his stomach, or to submit to the use of artificial respiration apparatus or to travel to a distant climate at great financial loss. All these are extraordinary means and therefore not obligatory.

However, there may be certain extrinsic circumstances making the use of extraordinary means mandatory from a moral point of view. Thus, a man who is the only support of his wife and three children may for their sake be obliged to take even extraordinary means to preserve his life. In many cases, just what constitutes ordinary means or extraordinary means might be very difficult to determine.

A man has the right to take extraordinary means to preserve his life but, usually speaking and apart from particular circumstances, he does not have the duty. In this connection we should

[2] *Loc. cit.*

say that the rights of a patient imply a correlative obligation incumbent on medical personnel. If a person has the right to a particular medical procedure, the doctor and nurse charged with his care have obligations accordingly.

The principle of ordinary means is summed up by Pius XII:

> Natural reason and Christian morality say that man (and whoever is entrusted with the task of taking care of his fellowman) has the right and the duty in case of serious illness to employ the measures necessary for the preservation of life and health.
>
> Normally one is held only to use ordinary means—according to circumstances of persons, places, times and culture—that is to say, means that do not involve any grave burden for oneself or another.
>
> A stricter obligation would be too burdensome for most men, and would make the attainment of our higher, more important good too difficult. Life, health, and all temporal activities are in fact subordinated to spiritual ends.
>
> But on the other hand, a man is not forbidden to take more than the strictly necessary steps to preserve life and health, as long as he does not fail in some more serious duty.[3]

The Principle of Subsidiarity

The principle of subsidiarity is basically a principle of Catholic sociology; but it has moral implications, and an appreciation and understanding of this principle will help those who are in administrative positions to formulate policies with greater justice and prudence.

The principle of subsidiarity was formulated by Pope Pius XI in his famous encyclical on social justice:

> This is a fundamental principle of social philosophy, unshaken and unchangeable. Just as it is wrong to withdraw from the individual and commit to the community at large what private enterprise and industry can accomplish, so too it is an injustice, a grave evil and a disturbance of right order for a larger and higher organization to arrogate to itself functions which can be performed efficiently by smaller and lower bodies. Of its very nature, the true aim of all social activity should be to help individual members of the social body, but never to destroy or absorb them.[4]

[3] *Loc. cit.* Extracts.

[4] *Quadragesimo Anno*, Pope Pius XI.

This principle is restated and confirmed by Pope John XXIII in his own encyclical on the social order.[5]

This principle might simply be stated: *What can be done by an individual or lower group should not be done by a higher group.* Thus if an individual nursing school is capable of carrying on an efficient training program and willing to do so, then the state or any federation of nursing groups should not interfere.

In the field of nursing, of politics, of sociology, the fundamental principle with moral overtones stands: What needs to be done should, if possible, be done by an individual or private group; if this is not possible then it should be done by the lowest possible unit of society.

Says Pope John XXIII: It is "wrong to withdraw from the individual and commit to the community at large what private enterprise and industry can accomplish." Consequently, there must be no interference with the "right that the individual persons possess of being always primarily responsible for their own upkeep. . . . Experience shows that where the personal initiative of individuals is lacking there is political tyranny."[6]

The Principle of Totality

The whole is greater than any of its parts. The question often arises: is it lawful to sacrifice a member of the body for the good of the whole body? The answer, of course, is yes since the body as a whole is more important than its individual parts.

Epikia

Epikia (also spelled epikeia) *is the reasonable presumption that the authority making a law would not wish to bind a person in some particular case*, even though the case is covered by the letter of the law. This may not be used if one could easily approach one who has authority to dispense from the law, nor may it be applied in cases

[5] Cf. *Mater et Magistra*, Pope John XXIII, 1961.
[6] Pope John XXIII in the encyclical *Mater et Magistra*.

of laws that would invalidate an action. It is based upon the keeping of the spirit of the law rather than the mere letter of a law. Civil law, for instance, forbids a nurse to put a patient in restraint on her own authority. A disturbed patient becomes dangerous, and no doctor can be contacted for a prolonged period of time. She might, by virtue of epikia, use restraints in the emergency.

Another example would be a policeman given orders not to go beyond his beat. He suspects a crime is being committed in the next block. He goes beyond his beat to prevent a crime, since there is no time to contact his superiors for permission.

Moral Maxims

One who acts through an agent is himself responsible. (Qui facit per alium facit per se.)

A patient in a hospital asks the nurse for reading matter which she knows is obscene. The nurse, realizing that this would be wrong, tells the orderly to bring the requested reading so that she then will not be responsible. Actually the nurse is responsible in arranging an occasion of sin through another person. Or again, a nurse, knowing contraception is immoral but wishing to give advice and encouragement to a friend in this matter, asks another nurse to give the advice so that she will not be doing anything wrong. This nurse is responsible by acting through a third party as her agent.

No one is obliged to betray himself. (Nemo tenetur se prodere.)

If a person commits a moral infraction, he is obliged to seek God's forgiveness and to repair whatever harm he has caused to the extent that could be reasonably expected. For instance, if a Catholic stole a considerable amount of money, he should confess the sin and make restitution for what was taken. He is not obliged, however, to identify himself as the thief or to turn himself in to the police.

In doubt, one may do what is generally done. *(In dubio judicandum est ex communiter contingentibus.)*

A nurse, having just received her registration, takes employment at a hospital with a reputation for good moral standards. She knows several Catholic nurses who have been working there and admires them for their good lives. After working for three days in the nursery, she is requested by the charge nurse to take a Jewish infant to the chapel for a ceremonial circumcision. Thinking that this might constitute cooperation in the religious services of another religion, she hesitates; but the charge nurse assures her that all nurses working in the nursery, including Catholics, customarily take infants to the chapel. Our young nurse has no time to contact a priest; the rabbi is waiting; the charge nurse is handing her the infant; everyone else is very busy; and the babies are all screaming, making it impossible for her to think. She should bring the child to the rabbi, as requested, following the usual procedure of the department. Later, to settle her mind, she could talk it over with a priest.

An object cries out for its owner. *(Res clamat ad dominum.)*

Although possession is a presumption of ownership, this presumption will always yield to contrary facts. If then a valuable ring is found, proper steps must be taken to find the true owner. If an object has been stolen from A, sold by B to C, and later given by C to D, ordinarily D must return the object to A, its true owner.

Some people think that if they have stolen some money, restitution will be accomplished if an equivalent amount is given to charity. "I will put it in the collection basket on Sunday," they say. But this will not do. The money "cries out for its owner." You can understand this easily by imagining that you are the owner.

Restitution by donation to the common good or to charity is only in order when it cannot be made to the proper person. Moral advice is needed in many cases of theft.

No one can give what he does not have. (Nemo dat quod non habet.)

This principle might be applied in many varied circumstances of nursing. For instance, a nurse has stolen an amount of money and does not have it to pay back at the present time. She wonders whether she may go to confession since she cannot make restitution. She may go to confession if she cannot pay the money back right now and need not trouble herself (no one can give what she does not have) but must promise to pay back the money when it becomes possible.

Possession is nine-tenths of the law. (Melior est conditio possidentis.)

Although the laws relative to justice and rights are complicated to apply at times, this one fundamental norm can be of help in determining a true owner. It, of course, must always yield to contrary facts that are established. If, for instance, a ring is now in the possession of a certain individual, presumption is that it belongs to him until the contrary is proved.

The end does not justify the means.

One common fallacy of the present day's moral thinking is that if we have a good purpose in mind, then whatever steps we take to accomplish that purpose are justified. A family that thinks a patient's tranquility will be disturbed if he realizes he is dying and tells him a lie as to his physical condition is doing wrong. Their good purpose has been accomplished by an immoral means. In any case in which an act is immoral, it does not become moral because it is done for a good purpose. To steal from a wealthy person in order to give money to a poorer person is wrong. It is wrong for a doctor to administer a lethal dose of drugs to a patient in order to terminate his suffering and eliminate a financial burden on the family.

Defects of nature may be corrected. (Licet corrigere defectus naturae.)

This general norm is almost instinctively accepted by all. If, for instance, a child is born with six fingers on each hand, there is no moral question in operating to remove the extra members. If a man has seriously scarred his face, even though otherwise he is perfectly healthy, plastic surgery may be utilized. This maxim may also be expressed in this way: "Everyone has a right to be normal." Therefore the taking of pills to establish regularity of the menstrual cycle can be permissible.

No one is a judge in his own case. (Nemo judex in propria causa.)

In making a decision relative to ourself, our judgment is warped often by nonessential details. Not uncommonly we are biased in our own favor. Or, from another aspect, a scrupulous person may be too harsh on himself. To seek moral and spiritual advice from the proper person is often very much in order.

Accessories belong to the principal object. (Accesorium sequitur principale.)

Ordinarily a minor accessory added to an object in such a way that it cannot be separated from it really becomes one with the principal object, and its ownership is determined thereby. Suppose two nurses are roommates. One has a painting, and the other agrees to have it laminated at her expense and put it on their wall. Later they separate, and the second nurse says that since she had the picture laminated she should take it with her. The first nurse says that the painting itself is hers even though embellished at some expense. Actually, the first nurse who owned the original picture has a right to the picture in its more expensive present state. She should reimburse her roommate for the expense incurred.

If one is willing to cooperate in an act, no injustice is done to him by the act. (*Scienti et volenti non fit injuria.*)

John has some secret that it may be embarrassing to reveal. Only James shares this secret, and he may not reveal it. However, the time comes when both John and James agree to tell Anthony. James is doing no injustice to John since John cooperates in revealing the secret.

A physician, wishing to test the effect of a new medication, agrees to give all services, treatments, and medications free providing the patient volunteers to act as a test case. The patient agrees willingly. However, the medication fails to cure him. He then complains to the doctor for subjecting him to the test. This is not a legitimate complaint. No injustice was done.

A very little is equal to nothing. (*Parvum pro nihilo reputetur.*)

The spirit of the law rather than the letter of the law is the important thing. Very often a minute violation of the letter of the law may be considered as no violation. This would be in the mind of the lawmaker. In a particular hospital it is forbidden to the employees to take medical supplies. A nurse takes two aspirin tablets for a headache without telling anyone. This is so small a matter that it is equal to nothing.

If a person finds a coin of trifling value, he need not take steps to find the owner since it is so small.

A little more or less does not change the substance of an act. (Plus minusque non mutat speciem.)

A man, for instance, who knows that intemperance in drinking is a problem for him, and that he has gotten into this trouble by taking 12 cocktails a day, says that he will only take 11. This minor difference will not change the morality of his guilt.

The recovery room procedure in a certain hospital cautiously requires that pressures be checked every 15 minutes. Patient A has reacted and seems in good condition; patient B is wheeled in in critical condition and needs special attention. The charge nurse omits one pressure check on patient A. This need not trouble her conscience; substantially, he is being given excellent care. The omission is so small as to amount to nothing.

Laws imposing an obligation may be given as narrow an interpretation as possible. (Odiosa restringenda sunt.)

Relative to the interpretation of laws, on the one hand a law giving a privilege may be interpreted in as broad a way as possible, and on the other hand a law restricting our liberty may be given the most narrow interpretation.

For instance, if the index of forbidden books says that any book by a certain author is forbidden, then we need not extend this to magazine articles by that author. Excommunication is attached to the crime of abortion; if a woman attempts an abortion and it does not result, she is not excommunicated, although of course she committed a serious sin.

No one is held to the impossible.
(Ad impossibile nemo tenetur.)

In the moral field, certainly God would not expect any person to do what is impossible or unreasonable. There is, for instance, a duty of returning stolen goods or money. A person who does not have the goods or money to return but is sorry, and as a Catholic goes to confession, is certainly forgiven and is not held to return the goods or money until such time as this may become possible. A nurse who is told to care for an unreasonable number of patients and who becomes worried that she is neglecting her duty, because she is physically incapable of carrying out all the details commanded, should remember this principle in settling her conscience.

A doubtful law does not bind.
(Lex dubia non obligat.)

A doubtful law is one which may not actually exist in fact or, if it does exist, may not apply to the situation at hand. The first obligation is to make a proper investigation in order to clear up the doubt. Only after sufficient diligence has been employed in proportion to the importance of the law and circumstances, and doubt concerning the existence of the law or its interpretation or application still exists, may this moral maxim be employed.

For example, a Catholic is doubtful whether he may eat frogs' legs on Friday. He takes steps to clarify his mind, but there is still some doubt. He may eat the frogs' legs, provided he has taken reasonable steps to banish the doubt.

Passion does not usually arise
from things to which we are accustomed.
(Ex assuetis non fit passio.)

Much of the regularly accepted clothing of our day would have been scandalous a hundred years ago and perhaps constituted a serious occasion of sin. Today's modest clothing, although more revealing than that of former times, does not constitute an occasion of sin because we are accustomed to it. Basic morality never changes —adultery will always be a mortal sin—but what constitutes a temptation may change according to circumstances. Something that would constitute a strong temptation to a high school boy might be utterly boring to a gynecologist.

Sacraments were meant for the good of souls. (Sacramenta propter homines.)

The sacraments are outward signs instituted by Christ to give grace, as for example extreme unction (given in danger of death), Holy Communion, confession. "Sacraments were meant for the good of souls" means in effect: "In doubt, give the sacraments." For instance, in an emergency when there is doubt if a person is alive, extreme unction should be administered. If there is doubt whether an infant is alive and it has not been baptized, it should be baptized at least conditionally.

The salvation of souls is the highest law. (Salus animarum suprema lex.)

In all things our ultimate judgment should be "Is what I am doing best for my own and others' eternal salvation?" The doctor who performs immoral operations may make money in so doing, but he must ask himself: "Is what I am doing morally good and helpful for my eternal salvation?" The nurse who is torn between assisting at immoral procedures or losing her good position may help to clarify her mind by remembering this principle.

Topics for Discussion

Items may be true, partly true, erroneous, or unsolvable. First judge, then discuss.

1. Can you think of any additional "moral proverbs" that might be helpful guides?

2. What are some medical procedures that would be considered as ordinary means? What are some that would be considered extraordinary means?
3. In light of the principle of subsidiarity, are there any aspects of medical care that are the proper province of the national government?

Cases for Solution

1. A policeman wants to place an illegal bet. He asks his wife to do this for him so that he cannot be criticized for conduct unbecoming an officer. He says that betting is not immoral, after all, and so accomplishing his end in this way will be all right.
2. A nurse works in a hospital where various types of sterilizations are done. Not having had any course in medical ethics, she is very doubtful about their morality. But having heard that in doubt one may do what is usually done, she cooperates in the operations.
3. A nurse reads only five pages of a 250-page obscene book, saying that this is so little a part of the book it does not matter.

References for Further Study

Bourke, V. J. *Ethics: A Textbook in Moral Philosophy*, New York: The Macmillan Company, 1953.

Ford, C., and Kelly, G. *Contemporary Moral Theology*, Westminster, Md.: The Newman Press, 1960, Vol. I.

Jone, H., and Abelman, U. *Moral Theology*, Westminster, Md.: The Newman Press, 1953.

Kenny, J. P. *Principles of Medical Ethics*, Westminster, Md.: The Newman press, 1962.

MacAllister, J. *Ethics: with Special Application to the Nursing Profession*, Philadelphia: W. B. Saunders Company, 1947.

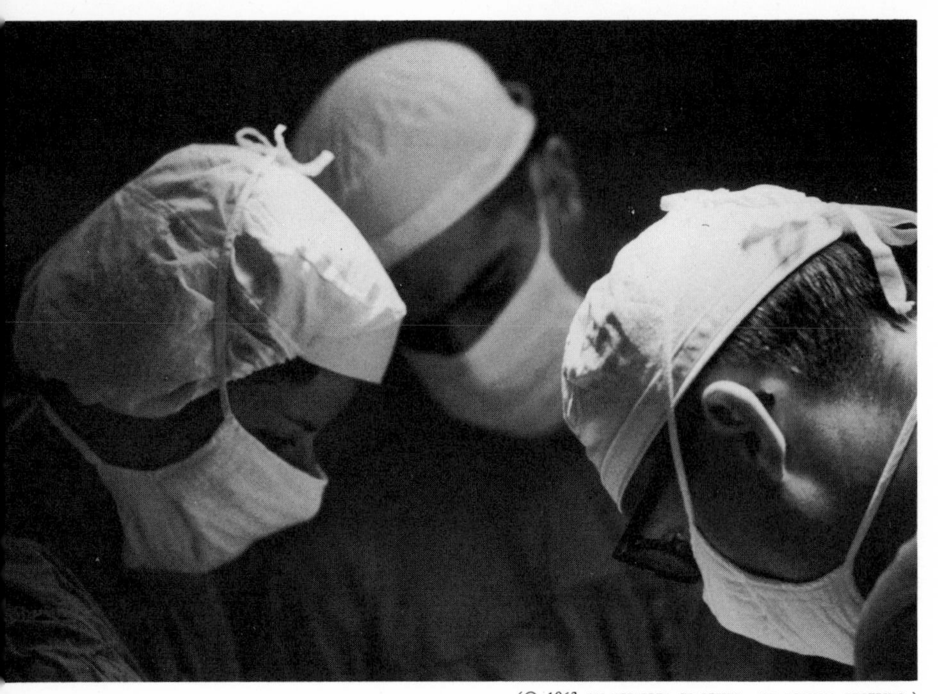

St. Vincent's Hospital, New York.

CHAPTER 6

The Morality of Cooperation

Formal cooperation · Material cooperation · Moral norms

THE WORD "COOPERATION" comes from the Latin word *cum*, which means "with," and *operari*, which means "to work." This gives us an excellent definition of cooperation. *Cooperation is working with another in the performance of an action.* The action may be good or evil. However, moral problems arise only when the action is evil.

The principles we are enunciating in this section apply to assistance in any immoral action. However, for most practical purposes in the nursing profession, they pertain to assistance at operations.

Cooperation may be divided first of all into *formal* and *material* cooperation.

Formal Cooperation

Formal cooperation is that in which the cooperator wills the evil, either by an explicit act of the will or by an actual sharing in the evil act itself. Those who share in an evil act sometimes say that they do so unwillingly. However, this is merely a way of saying that they are reluctant. If they were unwilling in the absolute sense of the word, they would not assist in the evil act at all. Since we are never allowed to will evil, formal cooperation in evil is always sinful. The assistant surgeon, who is actually performing some part of an immoral operation, formally cooperates in evil.

Material Cooperation

Material cooperation is that in which the cooperator performs an act which in itself is not wrong, though it is used by the principal agent to help him commit sin. Under certain circumstances, such cooperation would be morally permissible. The ward nurse who prepares a patient for immoral surgery cooperates materially.

Here are examples of various types of cooperation: A gangster plans to murder a rival. He secures the cooperation of the local precinct police captain, who arranges that no squad car will be in the area while the crime is being committed. The captain's cooperation is formal because he wills the evil act. The criminal tells one of his henchmen to prepare the car by checking the gasoline and making sure that the motor is operating perfectly. This man cooperates materially but only remotely. Another member of the gang is assigned to drive the "get-away car." This man cooperates materially and proximately. A third man is assigned to hold the victim, while the leader of the gang kills him. This man cooperates formally by sharing the evil act.

Moral Norms

Formal Cooperation in Evil Never Allowed

The nurse, because of her training, is schooled in obedience. She carries out quickly and without question the orders of the doctor. However, we must never forget that the moral integrity of the nurse as an individual is superior by far to the commands of any doctor. Therefore, when the question of assistance at an immoral operation arises, it is entirely within the rights of the nurse to make a moral judgment and act in accordance with her conscience.

A nurse must never formally cooperate in immorality either by explicitly willing the evil or by directly sharing in the immoral act itself.

Material Cooperation in Evil Sometimes Allowed

Under what circumstances may a nurse materially cooperate by tolerating the evil?

Material cooperation consists in performing morally indifferent actions which make the operation possible. Those who cooperate materially do not perform immoral actions, but rather actions which are morally indifferent or good, and therefore allowable under certain circumstances. Such morally indifferent actions are performed by the anesthetist, scrub nurse, circulating nurse, and ward nurse.

A general rule which may be given regarding material cooperation is this: Material cooperation in an immoral operation is morally permissible when a sufficient reason exists. No medical condition is a sufficient reason for the performance of an immoral operation. Certain circumstances may exist, however, which would constitute a sufficient reason for material cooperation; for example, the fact that refusal would probably result in dismissal.

Proportionate Reason Required for Cooperation in Evil

Just what constitutes a sufficient reason will vary according to the proximity to the immoral act itself. Material cooperation may be either proximate or remote. *Proximate cooperation* is that which is quite intimately connected with the immoral operation. An example of proximate cooperation would be that performed by the scrub nurse. Because of the very intimate connection of proximate cooperation with the evil act, a very grave reason is necessary in order that such cooperation be morally permissible. On the other hand, *remote cooperation*, being less intimately connected with the evil act, is morally allowable for lesser reasons.

Exactly what reason is sufficient for cooperation in a particular case is a matter of accurate moral judgment. Some cases are very easy to judge. For example, the threat of being dismissed immedi-

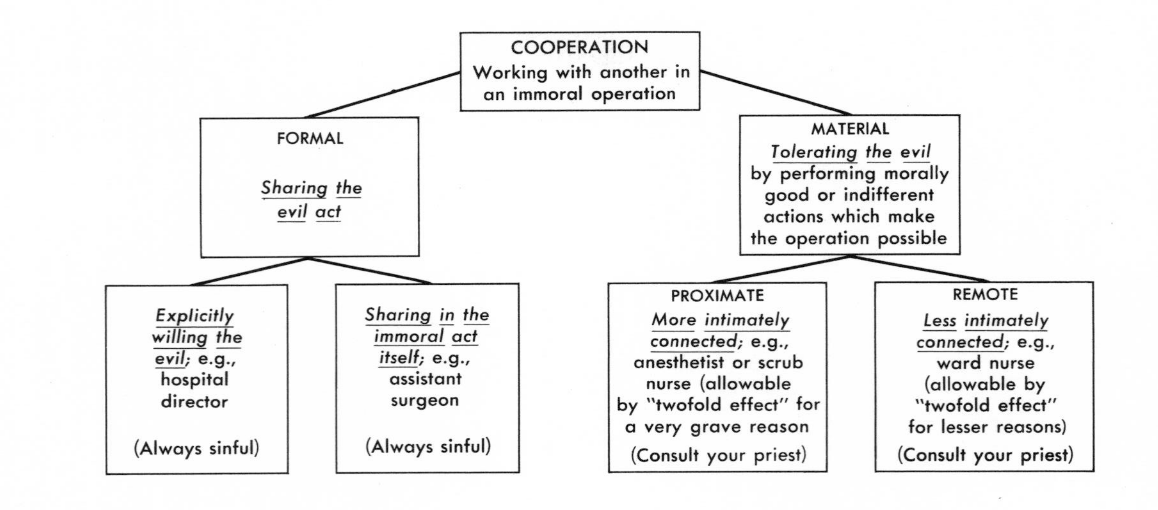

Figure 9. The morality of cooperation.

ately, combined with the knowledge that a new position will be almost impossible to obtain in the foreseeable future, is a very grave situation and would constitute a sufficient reason for proximate cooperation in a particular case. On the other hand, the possibility of slightly hurt feelings on the part of fellow workers is obviously not a grave situation.

When material cooperation is habitual, a proportionately graver reason is required. An isolated instance of material cooperation in an immoral act is more easily justified than repeated acts of the same sort. The nurse who finds herself in a situation in which she is asked to cooperate in an immoral operation on rare occasions may more readily do so in good conscience than the nurse who constantly finds herself in this position. It is difficult, for instance, to justify continued employment in a hospital that is notorious for constant violations of the moral law, no matter how remote the cooperation.

The more necessary one's material cooperation is to the performance of the act, the graver must be the reason to justify it morally. If the withholding of one's cooperation would result in the principal agent's being unable to perform the action, a much graver reason would be required than if others could easily be obtained to cooperate.

Resolving Doubts Regarding Cooperation

Between the obviously serious situations and those situations which are obviously not serious lies an entire field of situations which are difficult to judge. It is not possible to enter upon a detailed discussion of all the situations which arise in this regard. In practical cases concerning proximate and remote material cooperation in immoral operations, *a priest should be consulted* in order that a proper moral judgment may be passed. If it is impossible to consult a priest under the circumstances, the nurse will find it necessary to use her own judgment in accordance with her conscience. As soon as consultation is possible, a priest should be consulted, and a definite norm of conduct arrived at to govern future situations.

Topics for Discussion

Items may be true, partly true, erroneous, or unsolvable. First judge, then discuss.

1. A nurse at times will be called upon to cooperate in procedures which are morally wrong. However, apart from those nurses who may happen to be in a policy-making position, most nurses are required to take orders either from a physician or from hospital authorities and so cannot be held responsible.
2. List and discuss some of the situations in which a nurse would have to apply the principles of cooperation.

Cases for Solution

1. A nurse is called upon to assist at an operation which she knows is unnecessary. The patient is wealthy and the doctor wishes to use the money for the hospital which is in grave financial need. The nurse wonders whether she should cooperate in the operation.
2. A charge nurse lends her fountain pen to an orderly who wishes to write a letter. The nurse knows that the letter will be lewd and probably be an occasion of sin for the reader.
3. Immoral operations are frequently performed in a certain general hospital. Those who would object to taking part in these procedures would almost certainly be dismissed. Their departure would close the door to any hope of changing the situation in the future. May they remain and continue to give material cooperation?

References for Further Study

Aikens, C. *Studies in Ethics for Nurses,* Philadelphia: W. B. Saunders Company, 1938.

Connell, F. *Morals in Politics and Professions,* Westminster, Md.: The Newman Press, 1951.

Finney, Patrick, and O'Brien, Patrick. *Moral Problems in Hospital Practice,* St. Louis: B. Herder Book Co., 1956.

McFadden, C. J. *Medical Ethics,* 5th ed., Philadelphia: F. A. Davis Company, 1961.

SCIENCE RAISES AND SOLVES IMMENSE PROBLEMS IN ITS FIELD, BUT IT STOPS AT THE SACRED THRESHOLD OF THE SOUL.

PAUL VI

Address to the International Endocrinology Symposium, Dec. 16, 1963.

PART II

Moral and Ethical Principles of Nursing

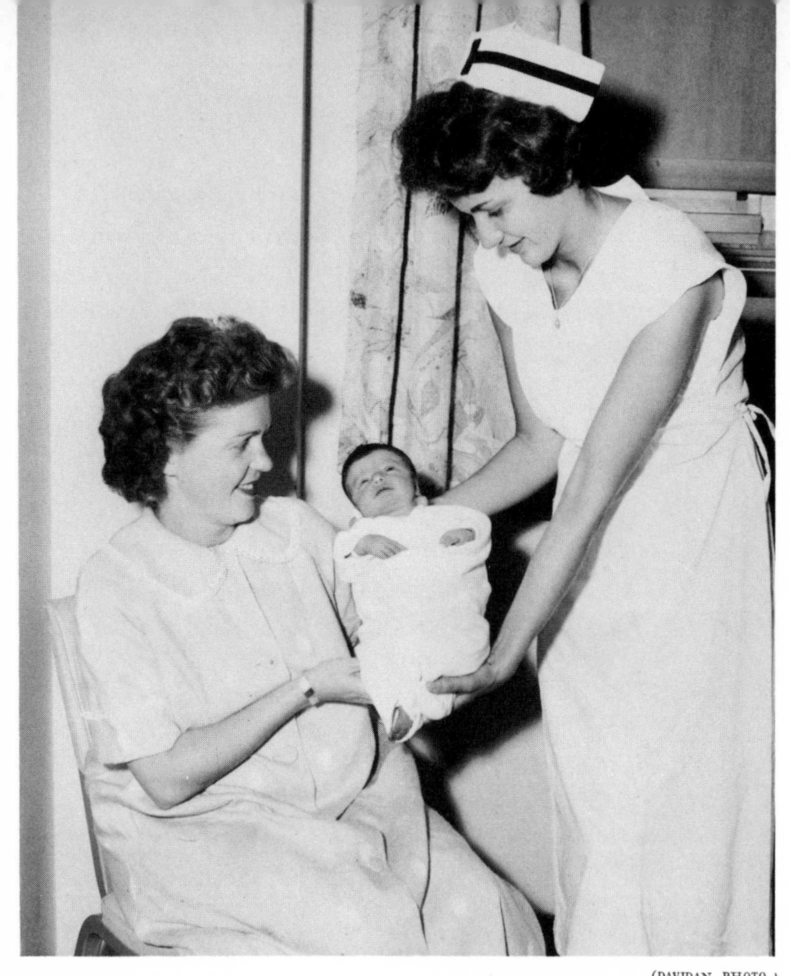

(DAVIDAN PHOTO.)

Holy Name Hospital, Teaneck, New Jersey.

CHAPTER 7

Principles Relating to the Origin of Life

Contraception · Total and periodic abstinence · Artificial insemination · Sterility tests

Contraception

"SIN AGAINST NATURE . . . shameful and intrinsically vicious . . . offense against the law of God . . . guilt . . . grave sin. . . ."

With such strong words from the pen of Pope Pius XI, contraception is branded. He wrote them in 1931 in his letter on Christian marriage. They are not, however, associated only with the thinking and the times of Pius XI. They represent the official attitude of the Catholic Church from its beginning up to the present day, an attitude which can never change for all future time.

In stark contrast to this attitude is the widespread use of contraceptives, openly approved by many groups, even religious bodies. Why this contrast? Why does the Catholic Church persist in refusing to change her teaching of former times?

Before we begin our discussion of this matter, we urge the reader to strive to examine the teaching of the Church objectively. We are living in sex-mad times. Sex is so overemphasized in our day that many people have acquired a false mental attitude in this regard. There are a few basic facts that may be called to mind profitably as we begin our treatment of contraception:

1. Majority opinion is not the norm of morality.
2. Widespread custom is not the norm of morality.
3. A good end does not justify an evil means.
4. If an act is evil by its very nature, nothing can make it good.
5. Our emotions should not be allowed to warp our moral judgment.
6. No one is a judge in his own case.
7. Christ said to His Church, "He who hears you, hears me."

Reproduction

At this point it would be well for the student to read the section on reproduction in her anatomy and physiology text and fix in mind the general facts regarding human reproduction. It is not necessary that an exhaustive study of details be made but simply that the matter be understood in its over-all aspects. The following definitions will be of value:

The *marriage act* is the intimate sexual union between a man and a woman in the normal course of which the sperm passes from the man into the vagina of the woman. It is also called "intercourse" or "coitus." Conception is the fertilization of the ovum by the union with the sperm.

Definition and Types of Contraception

Contraception is the direct prevention of conception; it is any interference with the procreative functions for the purpose of preventing conception or any interference with the marriage act itself. This prevention may be accomplished by the following means: (1) *Mechanical means*, whereby the seed is prevented from contacting the ovum; (2) *coitus interruptus* (withdrawal); (3) *chemical means*, whereby the life-giving elements are rendered incapable of performing their function; (4) *pharmacological means*, whereby the functions of the procreative faculties are suppressed; and (5) *surgical means* (sterilization), which consists in any operative procedure which renders an individual incapable of reproducing.

In speaking of contraception, the terms "birth control," "onanism," and "planned parenthood" are frequently used. However, one must judge from the particular context whether such terms are understood as synonyms for immoral contraception.

Arguments in Favor of Contraception

Many arguments are put forth in favor of contraception. For example, poor health, lack of money, eugenics, and overpopulation. Medical arguments in favor of contraception are based on physical conditions in which pregnancy would allegedly endanger life or health. Some of these conditions are obstetrical, such as toxemia, eclampsia, hyperemesis gravidarum, and pelvic disproportion. Some are medical in nature, such as heart disease, hypertension, renal disease, diabetes. Some doctors advocate the use of contraceptives in so many cases that there is hardly any point in listing them.

Opinion of Medical Profession as a Whole

Some time ago, a release from the Planned Parenthood Federation of America made the claim that in a poll of 15,000 physicians about 98 per cent approved birth control for reasons of health or for economic reasons. The distortion of fact was revealed later when it was found that of the 15,000 doctors polled, only 3,381 completed questionnaires were returned. So, in fact, the poll proved merely that less than 20 per cent favored birth control. The implication apparently intended by the Planned Parenthood Federation was an assurance to men and women of this country that artificial birth control is medically sound. Actually, the figures prove no such thing.[1]

[1] Cf. *The New York Times,* February 11, 1947. Cf. *America,* New York, March 8, 1947.

Opinions of Some Individual Physicians

Here are the comments of a few doctors on contraception:

Dr. Sigmund Freud:

Anxiety-neurosis appears in female persons—disregarding for the moment their predisposition—in the following cases: . . . d. whose husbands practice coitus interruptus or reservatus. . . . Congressus reservatus by means of condoms . . . is no less injurious than the others. Coitus interruptus is almost always harmful.[2]

Dr. William G. Morgan (former president of the American Medical Association):

Whenever man departs ever so little from the natural laws of the universe, destructive influences to a greater or lesser extent creep in, and in the laws of nature there is no provision for birth control through contraceptive devices. You have been told by some . . . that woman is aged in body and mind in proportion to the number of children which she bears. This is not borne out in fact. My experience in the practice of my profession over a period of thirty years confirms the truth of my declaration. Childbearing is the normal God-given function of womanhood.[3]

Dr. Raoul de Guchteneere (Belgian gynecologist):

It is not enough to say, as is maintained by the propagandists of Birth Control, that the regular use of contraceptive methods offers appreciable advantages to the individual and to the community: it is necessary that these should not involve serious disadvantages to the health of those who practice it. . . . It is not difficult to accumulate weighty evidence from doctors who are unbiased and especially qualified to judge to the effect that contraceptive prophylaxis is harmful.[4]

[2] Sigmund Freud, "The Justification for Detatching from Neurasthenia a Particular Syndrome: The Anxiety-Neurosis" (1894). First published in the *Neurologisches Zentralblatt*, 1895, Nr. 2. English translation quoted from *Sigmund Freud: Collected Papers*, vol. 1, New York: Basic Books, Inc., 1959, pp. 87-88. Authorized translation under the supervision of Joan Riviere. Quoted with permission.

[3] Dr. Morgan made this statement before the subcommittee of the Senate Judiciary Committee, during the hearings of May, 1932.

[4] Raoul de Guchteneere, *Judgment on Birth Control*, New York: The Macmillan Company, 1931, pp. 135 and 138.

Dr. Robert P. Odenwald (fellow of the American Psychiatric Association, writing with James H. VanderVeldt, O.F.M.):

Contraceptive practices disrupt marital unity much more than is suspected. In the marriage state, man and woman are to form a unity—man the father, woman the mother. In contraceptive intercourse there is no unity. "Planned parenthood" is an intended physical frustration of the natural sex functions and a psychological frustration of the natural instinct to propagate. Although differing in physical and psychological structure, both men and women are intended to complement one another. Sexual intercourse for married people is as much a psychological as a physical matter. To have marital relations for merely physical reasons and with the use of contraceptives was once characterized by a patient as an "unsatisfactory and delusionary act." Such dissatisfaction leads to quarreling; and couples who are always quarreling will never have satisfactory sexual relations, since harmony of mind is just as important as unity of the body. . . . Contraceptive intercourse is regarded by some of its own proponents as both psychologically and physically unsatisfactory, if not harmful.[5]

In 1962, a survey was made of the Medical Advisory Committee of Planned Parenthood of Chicago, and the majority of physicians on this committee said that they would not prescribe oral steroid contraceptives to their own wives and daughters.[6]

Mr. George Cadbury of the International Planned Parenthood Federation reported that a poll of doctors at World Health Organization headquarters was taken in 1962 concerning the steroid pill, and no single doctor who was asked would advise his daughter to use it.[7]

Dr. Herbert A. Ratner, in a medical critique of oral contraceptives published in 1963, stated that in Puerto Rico (where the use of oral contraceptives had been widespread) medical authorities found that in four years nearly 50 per cent of all users suffered side effects. These effects ranged from nausea, abdominal distress, vomit-

[5] J. J. VanderVeldt and R. P. Odenwald, *Psychiatry and Catholicism,* 2nd ed., Copyright, 1957. New York: McGraw-Hill Book Company, Inc. Used with permission.

[6] Cf. Herbert A. Ratner, *Oral Contraceptives: A Medical Critique* published by National Catholic Welfare Conference, Washington, D.C., 1963.

[7] "World Wide Report," *Medical Tribune,* July 2, 1962.

ing, and nervousness to the increased growth of pre-existing uterine tumors.[8]

On the basis of competent medical authority, we must conclude that birth control is, to say the least, not the panacea that some would have us believe.

Diseases Traceable to Birth Control

A good many reputable physicians have listed certain pathologic conditions as traceable to birth control. The late and highly respected Dr. Samuel A. Cosgrove and his son, Dr. Robert Cosgrove, of Margaret Hague Maternity Hospital, Jersey City, concur in this statement: "Sterility with and without pelvic infection, various neuroses (even psychoses) and much plain unhappiness and marital discord are all strongly pertinent."

Evolution of Protestant Opinion on Birth Control

In 1908, Episcopal bishops at the Lambeth Conference had spoken against artifical birth control, and again in 1920 they decreed: "We utter an emphatic warning against the use of unnatural means of avoidance of conception." However, in 1930 their stand was reversed: "We cannot condemn the use of scientific methods for preventing conception which are thoughtfully and conscientiously adopted."[9] In 1934 the Episcopal Church of the United States went on record as giving its approval to birth control. The Federal Council of Churches of Christ in America also decided in favor of artificial birth control, declaring "Careful and restrained use of contraceptives by married people is valid and moral."

In 1954 the ninety-fifth annual convention of the Augustana Evangelical Lutheran Church, speaking for 500,000 Protestants approved birth control in these words:

[8] Ratner, *op. cit.*

[9] Cf. Richard Ginder, *Planned Parenthood*, New York: Catholic Information Society, pp. 6-7.

An unrestrained production of children without realistic regard to God-given responsibilities involved in rearing children . . . may be as sinful and as selfish . . . as is the complete avoidance of parenthood. . . . The power to reproduce is His blessing, not a penalty, upon the sexual relationship in marriage.

The complete reversal of Protestants in their teachings on birth control can scarcely be upheld in the light of an immutable moral law.

Fundamental Catholic Teaching on Contraception

The fundamental Catholic teaching regarding contraception is clearly stated by Pope Pius XI in his letter on marriage:

No reason, however grave, may be put forward by which anything intrinsically against nature may become conformable to nature and morally good. Since, therefore, the conjugal act is destined primarily by nature for the begetting of children, those who in exercising it deliberately frustrate its natural power and purpose sin against nature and commit a deed which is shameful and intrinsically vicious.

Small wonder, therefore, that the Holy Bible bears witness that the Divine Majesty regards this horrible crime with greatest detestation and at times has punished it with death.

The Catholic Church, to whom God has entrusted the defense of the integrity and purity of morals, standing erect in the midst of the moral ruin which surrounds her, in order that she may preserve the chastity of the married state from being defiled by this foul stain, raises her voice and proclaims anew: *Any use whatsoever of matrimony exercised in such a way that the act is deliberately frustrated in its natural power to generate life is an offense against the law of God and nature, and those who indulge in such are branded with the guilt of a grave sin.*[10]

Twenty-one years later, the succeeding Pope, Pius XII, in his allocution of October 29, 1951, reiterated the same teaching in these words:

Any attempt on the part of the husband and wife to deprive this act of its inherent force or to impede the procreation of a new life,

[10] Pope Pius XI, Encyclical on Christian Marriage, Dec. 31, 1930.

either in the performance of the act itself, or in the course of the developement of its natural consequences, is immoral, and furthermore, no alleged "indication" or need can convert an intrinsically immoral act into a moral and lawful one.

This precept is as valid today as it was yesterday, and it will be the same tomorrow and always, because it does not imply a precept of human law, but it is the expression of a law which is natural and divine.[11]

Catholic Teaching is Based on the Nature of the Act

Marriage [continues Pius XII], as a natural institution, is not ordered by the will of the Creator towards personal perfection of the husband and wife as its primary end, but to the procreation and education of a new life. The other ends of marriage, although part of nature's plan, are not of the same importance as the first. Still less are they superior. On the contrary, they are essentially subordinate to it.

Does that mean a denial or a diminishing of what is good and right in the personal values which result from marriage and from the marriage act? Certainly not, because in marriage the Creator has destined human beings, made of flesh and blood and endowed with a mind and a heart, for the procreation of new life, and they are called to be the parents of their offspring as human beings and not as irrational animals.

All this is therefore true and willed by God; but it must not be disjoined from the primary function of marriage, that is, from the duty to the new life.

It follows that it is for you to tell the fiancé, or the young wife who comes to discuss with you the values of married life, that these personal values in relation to the body, sense or spirit, are really good and true, but that the Creator has put them in the second place in the scale of values, not the first.

The Creator in His goodness and wisdom has willed to make use of the work of the man and the woman to preserve and propagate the human race, by joining them in marriage. The same Creator has arranged that the husband and wife find pleasure and happiness of mind and body in the performance of that function. Consequently, the husband and wife do no wrong in seeking out and enjoying this pleasure. They are accepting what the Creator intended for them.

This, therefore, is the rule to be followed: *The use of the natural generative instinct and function is lawful in the married state only, and in the service of the purposes for which marriage exists.*

[11] Pope Pius XII, Allocution of October 29, 1951.

The act is completely subordinate and ordered to the great and unique law, "the generating and educating of children," that is, to the fulfillment of the primary end of marriage as the origin and source of life.

The seriousness and holiness of the Christian moral law does not permit the unrestrained satisfying of the sexual instinct, nor such seeking merely for pleasure and enjoyment.

Nature has given the instinctive desire for pleasure and sanctioned it in lawful wedlock, not as an end in itself, but in the service of life.[12]

Light of Reason Dulled by Passion

We now return to the words of Pius XI, who issues a very practical warning against a dangerous pitfall which often entraps human beings.

Everyone can see to how many fallacies the way would be open, and how many errors would be mixed with the truth, if it were left solely to the light of each individual's reason to discover the truth. . . . And if this is applicable to many other truths of the moral order, we must pay all the more attention to those things which pertain to marriage, where the inordinate desire for pleasure can attack frail human nature and easily deceive it and lead it astray.

The Role of the Church

On this account [the Pope continues], in order that no falsification or corruption of the divine law may occur, but a true genuine knowledge of it may enlighten the minds of men and guide their conduct, it is necessary that a filial and humble obedience towards the Church should be combined with devotedness to God and the desire of submitting to Him.

Let the faithful be on their guard against the overrated independence of private judgment and the false autonomy of human reason. It is quite foreign to everyone bearing the name of a Christian to trust his own mental powers with such pride as to agree only with those things which he can examine from their inner nature, and to imagine that the Church, sent by God to teach and guide all nations, is not conversant with present affairs and circumstances. On the contrary, a characteristic of all true followers of Christ, educated or uneducated, is

[12] Pope Pius XII, Allocution of October 29, 1951. Extracts.

to permit themselves to be guided in all things that touch upon faith or morals by the Holy Church of God through its Supreme Pastor and Roman Pontiff, who is himself guided by Jesus Christ Our Lord.[13]

The Bible on Contraception

The first person in recorded history to use birth control was Onan, and his story is told in the book of Genesis. It is recorded that this man, "when he went into his brother's wife spilled his seed upon the ground. . . . And therefore the Lord slew him because he did a detestable thing."[14]

Detailed Application of Catholic Principles

Having stated fundamental moral teachings on the subject of contraception, we now proceed to the application of these principles to particular means of contraception and also to show their bearing upon the safe period method and sterilization.

Mechanical Means of Contraception

Mechanical means of contraception would include condoms and diaphragms. A condom is a sheath, usually of rubber, used to cover the penis in order to prevent the sperm from entering the vagina. A diaphragm is a cap worn over the cervix for the purpose of preventing the seed from entering the uterus. Use of these devices to prevent conception is intrinsically immoral.

It is well to distinguish between a diaphragm and a pessary. A pessary is a mushroom-shaped device with an opening, used to correct a pathologic condition, usually for cervical stenosis (os tightly closed). Actually, this is frequently used to make conception possible. Its use is moral.

[13] Pope Pius XI, Encyclical on Christian Marriage, December 31, 1930.

[14] Gen. 38:9-10. It is to be noted that this was not an act of adultery, since Onan, in accordance with Jewish law, had married his deceased brother's wife.

Coitus Interruptus

Coitus interruptus, or withdrawal, is specifically mentioned in the Bible as worthy of death, as we have already shown. Medically, chronic congestion of the prostate may occur in the male, while in the female a chronic congestion may result because the tissues are not deplethorized for a period of time. In both sexes there are unfavorable psychic reactions.

Chemical Means

Chemical means would include douches and jellies. This also is an unnatural interference and as such constitutes a mortal sin.

The immediate use of a water douche is thought by some people to be necessary for hygienic reasons. This is not true. If such a thing were done in good faith, there would of course be no sin. But if it were done with contraceptive intent, the bad intention would make the act a mortal sin, regardless of its effectiveness as a contraceptive practice. A douche after the passage of more than an hour would not be immoral because it would have no contraceptive effect.

Pharmacological Means

Pharmacological means of contraception would include pills and injections to suppress ovulation or to render the sperm ineffective.

At this point it becomes necessary to make a distinction. There is a moral distinction between those procedures which constitute a perversion of the natural act of intercourse, such as withdrawal or the use of a contraceptive douche, and those procedures which affect the functioning of the procreative organs, such as taking a medication which inhibits ovulation. The performance of the procreative act in a perverted or unnatural manner is intrinsically evil and is not morally allowable for any reason. On the other hand, surgical or pharmacological procedures that affect the procreative faculties are procedures that are indifferent in themselves and therefore admit at times of application of the principle of the twofold effect. When the twofold effect principle is applicable, the intention of the responsible party enters into the determination of the morality of the act. On the other hand, when the act itself is intrinsically evil, intention is not at issue; the act is always wrong.

The taking of a medication which inhibits ovulation (and therefore conception) is not in itself an act contrary to nature and intrinsically immoral. Therefore such a procedure cannot be condemned on the basis of intrinsic immorality. What governs the morality? In one word, the *purpose* of the act.

If a woman takes a medication for the direct and exclusive purpose of preventing conception, she commits a serious sin. However, if she takes the medication for the direct purpose of curing or alleviating a serious pathologic condition, such as endometriosis or dysfunctional uterine bleeding, no sin is committed, even though sterility may occur concomitant with the treatment. This is an application of the principle of the twofold effect. It should be noted, however, that if it is feasible to effect a cure without interfering with conception, the principle of the twofold effect could not be applied.

The same principles would hold true in any possible parallel male situation.

It would be morally permissible to take a medication in order to achieve menstrual regularity, even though temporary sterility would result. This falls under the principle that everyone has a right to be normal.

In certain cases of apparent sterility, some physicians have expressed the belief that the probability of conception is increased if ovulation is suppressed for a time. This procedure (ovulation rebound) is moral under the principle of totality. One function of the body is temporarily suppressed for the general good of the whole body. In other words, medication may be taken for the purpose of achieving fertility, even though ovulation is impeded

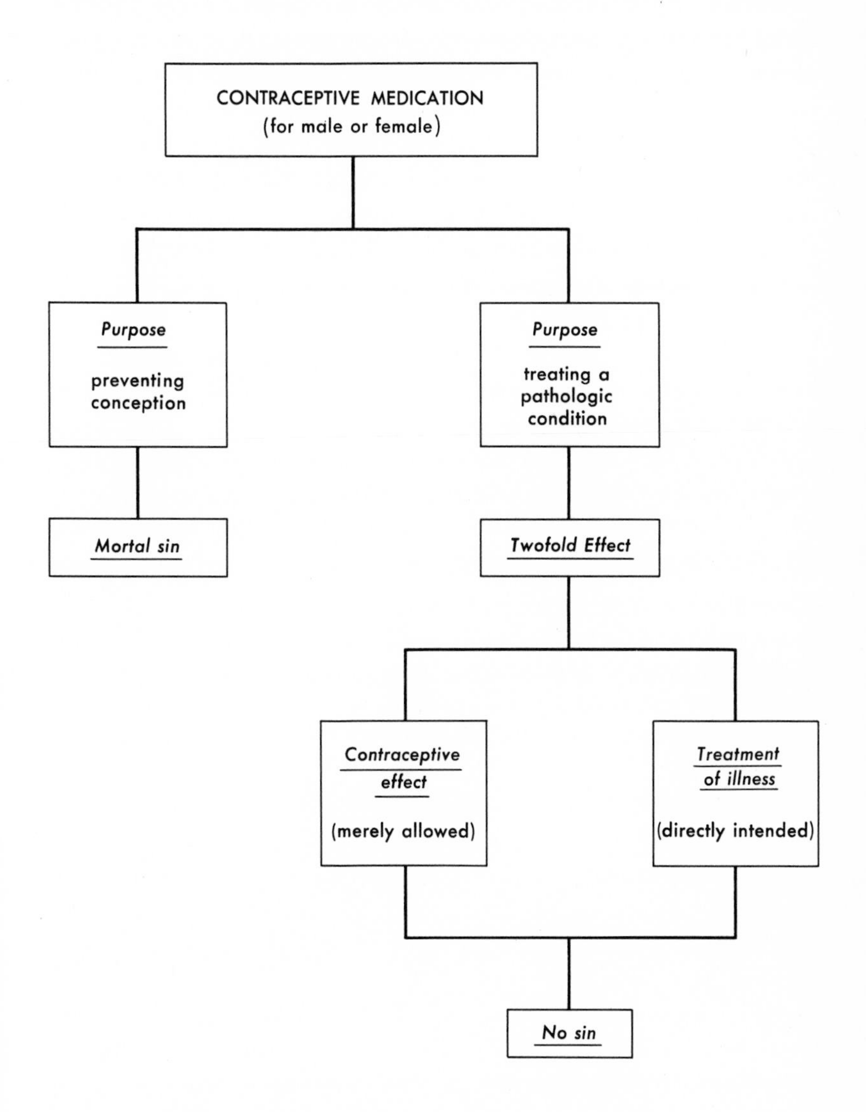

Figure 10. The morality of contraceptive medication.

as a means to the good end. The means used is not an evil one but an indifferent one, and its morality is therefore determined by its purpose. Of course, this moral conclusion is based on the supposition that harmful side effects from the medication are precluded.

Surgical Means

Surgical means of contraception—operations having sterilization as their direct purpose—will be treated in Chapter 9.

Total and Periodic Abstinence

In the course of married life there can be valid reasons why the conception of a child may be inadvisable. For example, severe financial difficulties, housing conditions, temporary illness of husband or wife, or certain severe physical or mental afflictions. In our preceding discussion we established that the use of artificial birth control is not allowable in any situation. Aside from artificial birth control there is a natural and lawful means which may be used when a sufficiently grave situation exists. This means is abstinence, which may be either total or periodic.

First Natural Method: Total Abstinence

There is only one sure way of preventing pregnancy, and this is by abstaining from intercourse. Contrary to popular opinion, this is by no means impossible. The question is not "Can I abstain?" but "Will I abstain?" We will discuss this more fully following our treatment of the rhythm method.

Second Natural Method: Periodic Abstinence

In most cases it is possible to calculate the days of the month when the female egg is present and conception could take place and likewise to calculate the days when no egg is present and conception could not take place. Therefore, it is possible to limit offspring by restricting intercourse to sterile periods. Since fertile and sterile periods succeed each other in regular pattern, their succession is called rhythm. The rhythm method is also called the safe or sterile period method.

Morality of Rhythm Method

The rhythm method may be used without sin when there is a good and sufficient reason. A trained moralist is the proper judge as to what constitutes a sufficient reason in a particular case. The doctor or nurse, not being trained in moral theology, is not competent in giving directions in this instance. Just as the moralist is incompetent in judging the physical condition of an individual, so the doctor or nurse is incompetent in judging the morality of a person's conduct. Catholics have as their guide the instructions of their confessor.

Marriage, which grants the right to the legitimate satisfaction of the sex instinct, also imposes the duty of providing for the conservation of the human race. This serious obligation cannot be put aside lightly. Except for a grave cause the conjugal debt may not be refused by one party; mutual consent is necessary. Moreover, ordinarily no one has a right to use the rhythm method when such use gives rise to grave danger of sin, either by one of the parties alone or with a third party. If, however, certain extraordinary circumstances are present, one party may have the right to demand the practice of rhythm, even though the partner is in grave danger of sinning, e.g., if danger of death would arise from pregnancy.

To summarize: The rhythm method ordinarily may be used only (1) with sufficient reason, (2) with mutual consent, (3) when danger of sin is excluded. Consultation with a priest is advisable in practically every case.

The advisability of consultation with a priest is based on the wisdom of the old axiom, "No one is a judge in his own case." Even when a layman is highly trained in theology, his judgment could be distorted by his feelings. Just as a prudent priest sometimes seeks the advice of a fellow priest, so the prudent layman will not make grave moral decisions affecting himself and his family without seeking moral advice. It is to be noted that the priest does not give permission to use the safe period method but makes a moral judgment as to the validity of the reasons alleged.

With regard to the required mutual consent, there might be cases where one of the parties will not consent, but his or her refusal is unreasonable. In such a situation, the injured party may use the safe period method without consent of the partner. Such a case would be rare, however, and furthermore would require careful moral appraisal—another good reason for consulting a priest.

Rhythm Method Not Contraception

It has been objected that the safe period method is contraception because it achieves the same effect. However, contraception is an interference with the marriage act, whereas the safe period method is not. There is an essential physical and moral difference between these two methods. *Contraception is the abuse, rhythm is the nonuse of marital rights.* The safe period method is abstinence—periodic abstinence.

The physical aspects of the safe period method are the subject of much controversy. The moral principles have always been clear: the method may be used without sin when there is good and sufficient reason.

If it is impossible to make the necessary calculations in a given case, or if the couple are unwilling to trust rhythm, there is only one lawful alternative—complete abstinence until conditions change.

The Popes and the Safe Period Method

In speaking of various moral aspects of the marriage union, Pope Pius XI stated:

> Nor are those considered as acting against nature who in the married state use their right in the proper manner, although on account of natural reasons involving either time or defects, new life cannot be

brought forth. For in matrimony as well as in the use of the matrimonial rights there are also secondary ends, such as mutual aid, the cultivating of mutual love, and the quieting of concupiscence, which husband and wife are not forbidden to consider so long as they are subordinated to the primary end and so long as the intrinsic nature of the act is preserved.[15]

Pius XII expressed this note of caution:

The moral lawfulness of such conduct would be affirmed or denied according as to whether or not the intention to keep constantly to these periods is based on sufficient and reliable moral grounds. . . . To embrace the married state, to make frequent use of the faculty proper to it and lawful only in that state, while on the other hand always and deliberately to seek to evade its primary duty without serious reasons, would be to sin against the very meaning of married life.[16]

Is Abstinence Possible?

In the light of what we have said regarding the morality of contraception and the morality of the safe period method, it can be seen that according to Catholic teaching, *when pregnancy is contraindicated by a grave and valid cause, abstinence is indicated.* Such abstinence may be either total or partial, according to circumstances.

Pope Pius XII points out that the decision on the contraindication of pregnancy because of a medical reason is the proper work of medical authority, not of a theologian; and he states that where circumstances definitely demand a "No," it would be wrong to prescribe a "Yes." Since every preventive practice and every direct attack on the life and development of the seed are forbidden and banned in conscience, there is only one thing to do: abstain.

It will be objected, however, that such abstinence is impossible, that heroism such as this is not feasible. This not true, and the reason may summed up in this manner: *God does not oblige us to do the impossible. But God obliges married people to abstain in certain cases. Therefore abstinence is possible.*

[15] Encyclical letter on Christian Marriage, December 31, 1930.
[16] Pope Pius XII, Allocution of October 29, 1951.

In confirmation of this argument, we have the doctrine of the Council of Trent, which quotes St. Augustine: "God does not command what is impossible; but when He commands, He warns you to do what you can and to ask His help for what is beyond your powers, and He gives His help to make it possible for you."[17]

> Do not be disturbed [says Pius XII], when in the practice of your profession and in your apostolate, you hear this clamor about impossibility. Do not let it cloud your internal judgment, nor affect your exterior conduct. Never lend yourselves to anything whatsoever which is opposed to the law of God and your Christian conscience. To judge men and women of today incapable of continuous heroism is to do them wrong. In these days, for many reasons—perhaps through dire necessity, or even at times under pressure of injustice,—heroism is being practiced to a degree and extent that in times past would have been thought impossible. Why then, if circumstances demand it, should this heroism stop at the limits prescribed by passion and the inclination of nature? It is obvious that he who does not want to master himself will not be able to do so; and he who thinks he can master himself, relying solely on his own powers and not sincerely and preservingly seeking divine aid, will be miserably deceived.[18]

The question, then, is not "Can I abstain?" but rather "Will I abstain with the help of God?" It is not that abstinence has been tried and found impossible, but rather that many people, finding it difficult, are unwilling to try it.

Artificial Insemination

Artificial insemination is any attempt to fertilize a female by a means which is a substitute for natural intercourse.

Artificial insemination cannot be considered exclusively from a biological and medical viewpoint. It is first and foremost a moral matter.

[17] Council of Trent, Session 6, Chapter 11. St. Augustine, *Nature and Grace*, Chapter 43, number 50, P.L. 44, p. 271.

[18] Address of October 29, 1951.

Artificial Insemination Between the Married

With regard to the lawfulness of artificial insemination in marriage, when fertilization is impossible in the usual way, it is sufficient for us to recall the principles of the natural law: Recourse to artificial insemination will not render a marriage valid between persons who are unfitted to contract marriage because of the impediment of impotency. Impotency is the inability to perform the marriage act.

It is lawful to use scientific methods to promote fertilization, once natural intercourse has taken place. This is sometimes referred to as "assisted insemination" to stress the fact that it is connected with a natural act of marriage.

It is never lawful for any reason to obtain seed by acts contrary to nature, such as masturbation or the use of a condom.

Artificial Insemination Outside Marriage

Artificial insemination outside marriage is to be condemned purely and simply as immoral. A child conceived in such conditions is, by this fact alone, illegitimate. The natural law dictates that the procreation of a new life may only be the fruit of marriage. Marriage alone safeguards the dignity of husband and wife. Marriage alone provides for the proper upbringing of the child.

Artificial Insemination by Third Party

Artificial insemination in marriage, with the use of the sperm of a third person, even with the consent of the husband, is more immoral than artificial insemination outside marriage because it is substantially adultery. Only marriage partners have mutual rights over their bodies for the procreation of a new life, and these rights are exclusive, nontransferable, and inalienable. Moreover, the husband has neither a moral nor a legal right to give anyone permission to inseminate his wife.

Nature imposes on whoever gives life to an infant the task of its preservation and education. Between marriage partners, however, and a child that is the fruit of insemination by a third person there is no moral or juridical bond of origin. The commonly used term "test-tube babies" is most appropriate.

Experience shows that artificial insemination is psychologically bad. Most children of such procedures are not loved by their parents as natural children are loved.

Pope Pius XII on Artificial Insemination

The Pope of Medicine, Pius XII, discussed the matter of artificial insemination and related topics thoroughly and clearly in his address to the Second World Congress on Fertility and Sterility, delivered on May 19, 1956. He sums up the Catholic teaching on artificial insemination in these words: "Artificial insemination violates the natural law and is illicit and immoral."[19]

Sterility Tests

Sterility is the inability to reproduce. A considerable number of marriages are childless, and some authorities believe that sterility exists in as high as 10 per cent of all marriages. Correction of this difficulty is of tremendous importance, and the number of couples seeking such medical aid is steadily on the increase.

Sterility on the part of the female may exist because of a number of abnormal conditions, many of which constitute challenging medical problems. They do not, however, present any moral problems, and so we can pass over them without comment.

[19] Cf. discourse on artificial insemination to Fourth International Convention of Catholic Physicians, October, 1949.

Sterility on the part of the male is not only more frequent but also gives rise to moral difficulties. This is so because the first step in the study of the problem is a laboratory examination of a sample of the semen of the individual concerned. The moral problem is posed by this question: How can a sample of semen be obtained without violating the moral law?

In making a moral judgment on this matter, it must be remembered that the good purpose in mind does not erase the moral principle that the specimen may never be obtained by immoral means. The end does not justify the means.

Immoral Means of Obtaining Specimen

It sometimes happens that a doctor will issue an order to the nurse to request a patient to produce a specimen of semen. The nurse should ordinarily refuse to carry out such an order when she has reason to believe that an immoral method will be used to procure it.

Masturbation to obtain a specimen for the laboratory is immoral. The act is intrinsically evil and therefore not allowable for any purpose.

The use of a condom to obtain a specimen is also intrinsically evil and not morally allowable. The use of withdrawal is immoral for the same reason.

It has been suggested that a perforated condom would provide a moral means of solving this problem.[20] We hold, however, with Father Connell[21] that such a method is immoral. The same may be said regarding withdrawal before emission is completed in order that part of the ejaculation may be saved as a specimen.

Moral Means of Obtaining Specimen

A method of collecting semen which is not opposed to the moral law has been devised by Dr. Joseph Doyle, of Boston. This is

[20] J. J. Clifford, S.J. "Sterility Tests and Their Morality," *American Ecclesiastical Review*, November, 1942, pp. 358-67.

[21] "The Catholic Doctor." *Ibid.*, December, 1944, p. 446.

known as the "cervical spoon method."[22] It should be suggested when immoral methods are proposed.

The cervical spoon method consists in the insertion of a special "spoon" under the cervix. The spoon in no way occludes the os of the cervix, and therefore conception is not inhibited. In normal coition a certain amount of sperm remains in the canal. Some of this is collected in the spoon. After the lapse of a minimum period of an hour to allow for further possible travel of the seed, the spoon is removed, placed in a container, and sent to the laboratory for examination.

Summary

In the light of all that we have said regarding problems related to the origin of life, we may now very briefly review the teaching of the Catholic Church.

Reason dictates that the primary purpose of the marriage act is the procreation of children. Nature provides pleasure in order to induce human beings to marry and perform the conjugal act and thus ensure the perpetuation of the human race.

A parallel situation can be cited in the matter of eating. Reason dictates that the primary purpose of eating is to sustain life. Nature provides pleasure in order to secure the survival of the individual.

The person who puts pleasure before the purpose for which nature intended any human function is upsetting the order of nature. If the matter involved is a serious matter, he commits a serious offense against nature and therefore against the Creator of Nature.

Contraception, then, is a sin against nature. As a result, it is classified as intrinsically wrong; that is, it is wrong under any circumstances. A person can allege many reasons why murder would be convenient in certain cases, but it cannot be allowed because it is intrinsically wrong. So also with contraception. One can allege reasons why it should be practiced in particular cases, but these

[22] Cf. Joseph B. Doyle, "The Cervical Spoon: An Aid to Spermigration and Semen Sampling," *Bulletin of the New England Medical Center, 10:*225-31, 1948.

reasons can never be sufficient because nothing permits us to violate the order of nature created by God.

Those who use the marriage act solely for pleasure, while preventing the purpose for which the act was naturally ordained, are upsetting the order of nature. They are doing an unnatural act and consequently a wrong act. They offend nature and therefore they offend God, who created nature.

The use of the generative instinct and function is lawful only in the married state and only in the service of the purposes for which marriage exists. It is completely subordinate to the primary end of marriage as the origin and source of life.

Topics for Discussion

Items may be true, partly true, erroneous, or unsolvable. First judge, then discuss.

1. A Catholic nurse urges a non-Catholic nurse to make use of "birth control pills" since the prohibition of the Catholic Church does not bind her.
2. Our civil life would be much more harmonious if the Catholic Church would confine her moral teachings to Catholics, especially on matters like birth control, which is purely a personal matter.
3. In the case of a childless couple, might not artificial insemination be a better answer than adoption? The adopted child is not related to the parents, whereas the child who is a product of insemination is a natural child of the mother.
4. The Church speaks with divine authority on moral matters.

Cases for Solution

1. A nurse is 32 years old, has a husband who is blind, and two small children. She wishes to use the safe period method to avoid pregnancy and continue working to support her family. Has she a sufficient reason?
2. A laboratory technician often examines samples of semen, and he finds out that a certain doctor obtains them by immoral means. Must he refuse to examine specimens sent in by that particular doctor?
3. You are a floor nurse. A Catholic patient is admitted in serious con-

dition, and she tells you not to call the priest because she has been using birth control.

4. You are a Catholic nurse. A non-Catholic patient confides to you that she uses a diaphragm. Knowing that the natural law binds everyone, what do you think you should do about this situation?

References for Further Study

Connell, Francis J. "Civil Legislation on Contraception," *American Ecclesiastical Review,* Washington, D.C., September, 1962.

Godin, Edgar, and O'Hanley, J. P. E. *Hospital Ethics,* Bathurst, New Brunswick, Canada: Hotel Dieu Hospital, 1957.

Kenny, John P. *Principles of Medical Ethics,* Westminster, Md.: The Newman Press, 1962.

McFadden, C. J. *Medical Ethics,* 5th ed., Philadelphia: F. A. Davis Company, 1961.

Marshall, John. *The Ethics of Medical Practice,* London: Darton, Longman and Todd, 1960.

Niedermeyer, Albert. *Compendium of Pastoral Medicine,* New York: Joseph F. Wagner, Inc., 1961. (Trans. by Fulgence Buonanno.)

O'Donnell, R. "Contraception and Rhythm," *The Nebraska Medical Journal,* April, 1937.

Pope Pius XI *Christian Marriage* (encyclical), New York: The Paulist Press, 1941.

Pope Pius XII *Moral Questions Affecting Married Life,* New York: The Paulist Press, 1951.

Schwitalla, A. "The American Medical Association and Contraception," *Graduate Nurses,* New York, 1938.

——— "The Moral Aspects of the Rh Factor," *The Linacre Quarterly,* January, 1947.

Solesmes, Monks of. *The Human Body,* New York: Daughters of Saint Paul, 1960.

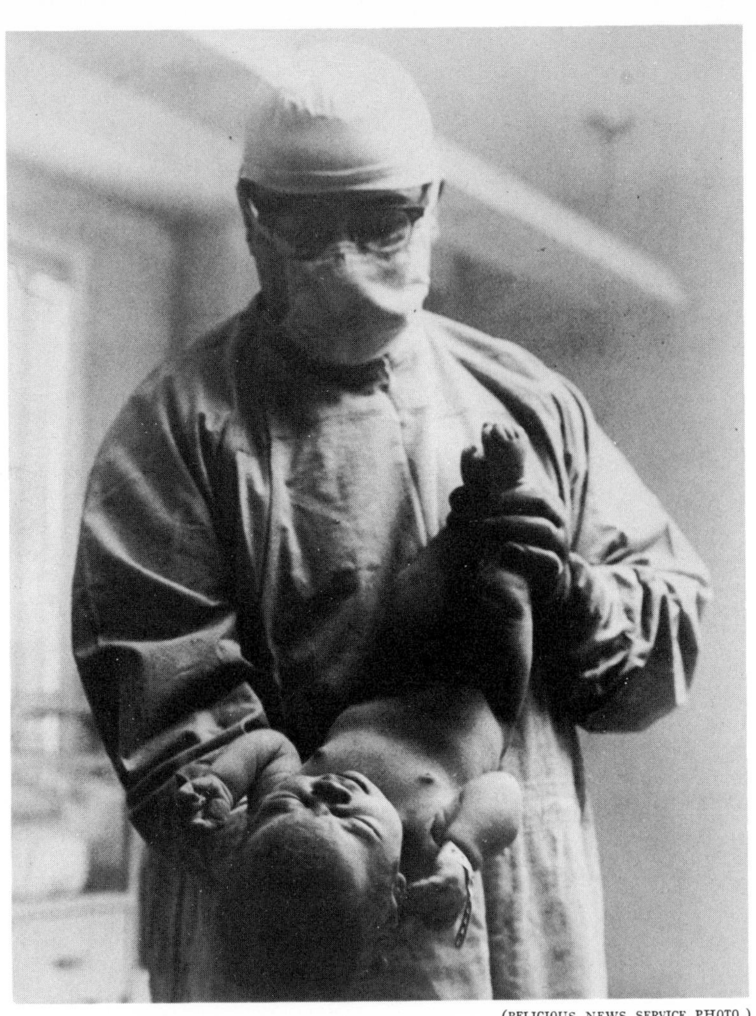

(RELIGIOUS NEWS SERVICE PHOTO.)

CHAPTER 8

Principles Relating to the Destruction of Life

The right to life · Abortion · Specific problems relative to the destruction of life · Induction of labor · Euthanasia · Administration of narcotics to the dying

The Right to Life

ONE CANNOT OWN ANYTHING until he is already alive. Life is a prerequisite to ownership. Therefore no man owns his life. *The owner of human life is not man but God*, who gave life to man.

Certain individuals with physical or mental defects, or both, have been given life by Almighty God. In some cases, human beings find it difficult to explain why God has done this. It is to be expected that our human intellects will be unable to fathom the purpose of the infinitely wise Creator in every single case. The existence of a problem in our limited human intellect does not bestow upon us the power and authority to adjudge God in error or to put out of existence a life that the infinite wisdom of the Creator has seen fit to send into the world.

Therefore, it follows that men have a right to their life by reason of the fact that God has made them custodian of it. It also follows that they have a duty to conserve life until such time as the Almighty sees fit to take it away.

The Right to Take Life

The direct taking of human life can be justified in only one situation: self-defense.

Self-defense may be personal, social, or national. It is personal when an individual finds it necessary to repel an unjust aggressor. It is social when society finds it necessary in order to arrest crimes of such magnitude that they threaten the very foundations of peaceful existence. It is national when a whole nation is attacked by an unjust aggressor. Therefore, at times, it is possible to justify killing in personal self-defense, capital punishment, or war. Moreover, what you may do for yourself, you may do for another in the same situation, such as killing (when necessary) a man who is unjustly attacking a third party.

Much of the material falling under this general heading does not fall within the scope of medical ethics, and its detailed treatment has no place here. Of practical importance to the nurse in this connection are euthanasia, abortion, the Catholic philosophy of suffering, and certain aspects of surgical ethics, all of which are treated under separate headings.

Results of Unjust Taking of Life

As soon as anyone is allowed to take human life for any reason besides legitimate self-defense against an unjust aggressor, the door is open to the most horrible crimes, and society becomes the victim of injustice, murder, fear, and suspicion. No one is secure in the possession of his life, and chaos and misery reign. This is what happened in Germany under Hitler, when euthanasia was made legal, and the government claimed the right to liquidate anyone considered useless to the state.

Adverse Public Sentiment

The general public is becoming aware of violations of God's dominion over life by certain members of the medical profession. As this awareness increases, there is a growing sense of fear and distrust that threatens the respect which should be associated with this great profession. How can a man respect you if he thinks you are one of those who murders unborn children? How can he help but fear you, if he thinks he may one day be put on the list of those you would like to kill because you feel they are no longer useful to society? The very man who asks you to commit a crime is the one who respects you least and distrusts you most.

Abortion and euthanasia, whether actually practiced or merely advocated in theory, are taking their toll. You cannot sow violations of natural law and reap the respect of mankind. Flee from the ugly truth as you will, the fact remains that there exists in the public mind a conviction that the hands of many doctors have been stained with innocent blood. Nurses who work by their side cannot long escape the same stigma.

Is this judgment on the part of the public justified? Justified or not, it illustrates the fact that the violation of the natural law has disastrous consequences.

In the matter of human life, if you restrict yourself to philosophy, human reason tells you that any direct attack upon an innocent human life is a violation of God's prerogatives and attacks the stability of society as well as the honor in which your profession is held. If you accept divine revelation, theology points to Almighty God thundering His curt prohibition from Mount Sinai. In either case, it adds up to this: "Thou shalt do no murder" (Exod. 20:12).

Abortion

Abortion is the expulsion of a nonviable fetus. This expulsion may be deliberate or accidental; it may be threatened, incomplete, or complete. Moral problems arise when the fetus is living.

Viability

Viability is the possibility of remaining alive outside the body of the mother. The fetus reaches viability approximately at the end of the twenty-eighth week of gestation. It may survive somewhat earlier if special incubation facilities are available.

Confusion of Terms

In the public mind, the term "miscarriage" indicates involuntary expulsion of a nonviable fetus, and "abortion" indicates a willful expulsion. In medical terminology the word "miscarriage" is almost never used, and the term "abortion" has a very broad meaning.

Lay misunderstanding of medical terminology often gives rise to difficulty and confusion. For example, certain female patients upon admission to a hospital often are startled and offended when required to sign a statement of this nature:

> I, the undersigned, a patient applying for admission to ———— Hospital, believe that I am in a condition of abortion. I hereby declare that neither the attending physician nor any person employed by or connected with the said hospital has knowingly performed any act which may have contributed to the induction of the abortion.

Many hospitals require this signing as a formality to protect themselves from possible legal complications.

Classification of Abortion

Abortion may be divided into three major classifications: (1) spontaneous, (2) indirect, and (3) direct. Spontaneous abortions may be threatened or inevitable, complete or incomplete. Direct abortions, which are also called "induced," may be either criminal or therapeutic.

Spontaneous Abortion

Spontaneous abortion is that which is caused by disease or accident. It is the unintentional expulsion of a fetus. It may occur in one out of seven or eight pregnancies, usually during the first three months. Spontaneous abortions are often caused by glandular abnormalities or generalized infections such as pneumonia, influenza, and syphilis. Sometimes vitamin deficiencies are a cause. Women who come into contact with radiation such as x-ray are in danger of abortion. A common cause is said to be sexual intercourse in the early months of pregnancy. Contrary to common belief, falls, blows, and overexertion are rarely a factor.

When there is bleeding, the outcome of which is doubtful, the abortion is known as a *threatened* abortion. On the other hand, when it appears certain that the fetus will be expelled, the term *inevitable* abortion is used. If the fetus has already been expelled but some secundines remain, the abortion is referred to as *incomplete*, a situation presenting no moral problem.

If the spontaneous abortion is merely threatened, in most cases bed rest and appropriate medications are the only treatments indicated. Termination by curettage, which is sometimes advised in this case, would be morally as well as obstetrically wrong. Packing, as well as the use of a tampon, would also be immoral under the circumstances.

Surgical Intervention in Inevitable Abortion

If a spontaneous abortion seems to be inevitable, that is, the cervix is dilating of its own accord, and the patient is hemorrhaging and is in immediate danger of bleeding to death, surgical intervention is indicated. The operation is referred to as dilatation and curettage ("D and C").

Surgical intervention is licit if the placenta has become detached, because then the fetus has already expired by reason of lack of oxygen. Before the placenta is detached, curettage would constitute a direct attack on the life of the fetus.

By the time the patient is brought to the operating room, the fetus has almost always been expelled. And of the rare few cases in which it has not been expelled, it is morally certain that the fetus is dead. Therefore, the doctor has moral certitude that there is no living fetus present.

Swift death by exsanguination (severe hemorrhage) threatens the mother, and in order to save her life the doctor proceeds upon the basis of his moral certitude.

Emptying the uterus is permissible when the physician is reasonably sure that the fetus is already dead or already detached.

In the case of an incomplete abortion, no moral problem exists, since the fetus has already been expelled.

Indirect Abortion

Indirect abortion is the foreseen (at least with probability) *but unintended loss of the fetus following upon a medical procedure necessary to preserve the life or health of the mother.* The fetus is in no way directly attacked, and the loss of fetal life is a secondary and unintentional consequence.

The removal of an acutely infected appendix might be necessary to save a mother's life, but there is great risk to the life of the fetus. Surgery at this time is permissible by reason of the principle of the twofold effect: the act is morally indifferent, it produces a good effect which does not follow from the evil effect, the motive is good, and the good effect at least equals the evil which may result. This situation is morally similar to tubal pregnancy or a cancerous uterus.

Direct Abortion

Direct ("induced") abortion is a deliberate termination of pregnancy, the only immediate purpose being the destruction of the fetus. Under this classification would fall criminal and therapeutic abortions.

Any Catholic who procures an effective induced abortion incurs an excommunication which can be lifted only by the bishop of the diocese or by a priest authorized by him. The Code of Canon Law of the Catholic Church (Canon 2350) states: "Persons who procure abortion, the mother not excepted, automatically incur excommunication reserved to the Ordinary[1] at the moment the crime takes effect." This penalty applies to both criminal and therapeutic abortions and includes the mother, those who formally cooperate in the procedure (such as nurses, doctors, interns), hospital authorities who sanction the procedure, parents or others who order or arrange it, and all who in any way formally cooperate in the crime through persuasion or advice.

Criminal abortion is one which is performed for no other reason than that the child is unwanted. Criminal abortion may be either self-induced or done by a professional abortionist.

Because of the manner in which criminal abortions are performed, they sometimes result in septicemia. The immediate dangers in these immoral procedures are hemorrhage and infection. Sterility often results. These patients are almost always gravely ill both spiritually and physically.

Criminal abortion is murder and is legally punishable as such in many places. Criminal abortion is therefore in ill repute morally, medically, and legally.

Therapeutic abortion is an abortion induced directly and deliberately for the purpose of saving the mother from death or illness. There is no moral distinction between therapeutic and criminal abortion: both are a direct attack on an innocent life. The principle of the twofold effect does not apply because any good which results arises by reason of the performance of an evil act. The health of one person is preserved by the direct murder of another person.

The official standing of the Catholic Church on this matter was given by Pope Pius XII:

[1] The Ordinary is the bishop in charge of the diocese, or his deputy.

Every human being, even a child in the uterus of its mother, has a right to life directly from God, and not from its parents or from any human society or authority. Therefore there is no man, no human authority, no science; there is no medical, eugenic, social, economic or

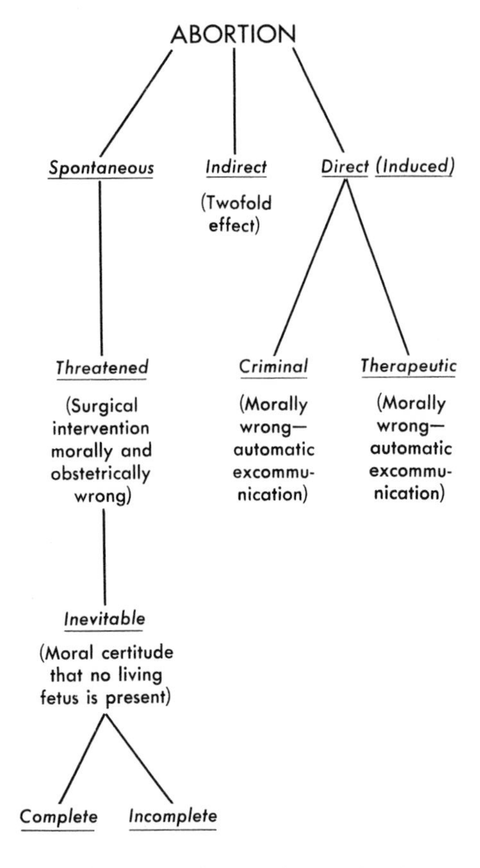

Figure 11. The morality of abortion.

moral "indication" that can offer or produce a valid juridical title to a direct deliberate disposal of an innocent human life; that is to say, a disposal that aims at its destruction, either as an end, or as a means to another end which might be in no way unlawful in itself. For example, to save the life of the mother is a very noble end; but the direct killing of a child as a means to that end is not lawful. The life of one who is innocent is untouchable, and any direct attempt or aggression against it is a violation of one of the fundamental laws without which a secure human society is impossible.[2]

Although morally wrong, therapeutic abortion is legal in many places. It is performed in cases of toxemia, hypertension, cardiac diseases, kidney diseases, certain types of mental diseases, pulmonary tuberculosis, hyperemesis gravidarum, and many less common conditions.

It has been said that the indications for therapeutic abortion are growing fewer, and that the procedure is becoming rare. Although it is certain that the "need" is growing less and less, there are few people who are familiar with modern medical practices who would use the word "rare" in speaking of therapeutic abortion. Indeed this matter is a constant source of difficulty for many Catholic nurses.

As far back as 1951, Dr. Roy J. Heffernan, of Tufts Medical College and Carney Hospital in Boston, speaking before the American College of Surgeons, emphatically declared:

Anyone performing a therapeutic abortion today does so because he is either ignorant of modern methods of treating complications of pregnancy or else he is unwilling to take the time to treat them. . . . Abortions are contrary to natural law. An unborn baby is human, and the medical profession is dedicated to preservation of human life.

Referring to the outstanding record of the Margaret Hague Maternity Hospital of Jersey City, New Jersey, Dr. Samuel Cosgrove told the American College of Surgeons in 1951:

We do not, in our hospital, feel we have "murdered" any mother by withholding therapeutic abortions. Heart disease, for example, under no circumstances is ground for an abortion because the handling of women in labor can be adroit enough to eliminate shock. . . . Therapeutic abortion not only carries a high death rate in itself, but is fraught with other hazards. . . . Such an operation is often followed by semi-invalidism, sterility, serious trauma, a guilt complex and frustration.

Dr. Robert Cosgrove, in an interview with the authors, added:

Therapeutic abortion has the risks of any (including criminal) interference. Legal assent does not prevent hemorrhage, infection, accentua-

[2] Allocution of October 29, 1951. Extracts.

tion of the disease for which the abortion was done, or psychic trauma. There is a very high incidence of psychic trauma. All the horrible things that happen in criminal abortions also happen in therapeutic abortions.

In Ziegel-Van Blarcom's *Obstetric Nursing*, the following comment is made: "With advances in medical treatment the indications for therapeutic abortion are becoming less and less, since many complicating conditions can now be more successfully treated during pregnancy than was formerly possible."[3] The passage of time and the outstanding record of such hospitals as the Margaret Hague Maternity Hospital are bringing to light the fact that good morals and good medicine may be closer than formerly believed.

If properly approached, hospital authorities are usually willing to arrange their schedules so that Catholic nurses are not required to assist at operations to which they have objections in conscience.

Baptism of the Fetus

A few comments should be made here relative to the baptism of a fetus. Probably from the instant of conception, and certainly from the point at which human physical characteristics appear, the fetus is endowed with an immortal soul and destined for union with God. Therefore every fetus should be baptized if the opportunity presents itself. This holds true regardless of the immaturity of the fetus and of the circumstances which have brought about its separation from the body of the mother. Details regarding baptism will be discussed in Chapter 11.

Disposal of Fetus

A fetus which has been baptized, even only conditionally, should be buried in consecrated ground if it does not involve too great inconvenience. An unbaptized fetus should be buried in unconsecrated ground, preferably the section of the cemetery reserved for the purpose.

[3] E. Ziegel and C. Van Blarcom, *Obstetric Nursing*, 5th ed., New York: The Macmillan Company, 1964.

If there is a good and sufficient reason, a fetus may be kept for study.

A fetus should be burned only to prevent the spread of disease.

A baptized fetus from a dead mother should be buried with her.

The nurse should strive to put into practice the ideals of the Church regarding disposal of fetuses insofar as this lies within her power.

Rape

The innocent victim of a criminal attack is allowed to eject or destroy the sperm before conception takes place. Unjust aggression is the moral basis which justifies the victim. The sperm may be removed from the vagina at any time after the attack, since conception does not take place there. However, if any means is used to remove it from the uterus or fallopian tubes, it must be employed before there is any probability that an impregnated ovum might be removed.

Pregnancy resulting from rape does not beget the right to procure abortion.

Specific Problems Relative to the Destruction of Life

Destruction of Fetal Life

Any direct attack upon the life of the fetus for whatever cause is immoral. Under this prohibition would come craniotomy, cephalotripsy, decapitation, and evisceration, when performed upon a living fetus.

Hyperemesis Gravidarum

Hyperemesis gravidarum (excessive vomiting in pregnancy) usually occurs previous to the time at which the fetus is viable.

The treatment is proper medical care and not a therapeutic abortion, which would be immoral. The Margaret Hague Maternity Hospital in Jersey City, New Jersey, has stated that in a 10-year period, without resorting to therapeutic abortion relative to hyperemesis gravidarum, there was not a single maternal death. The moral principles are clear; if the fetus is nonviable, termination of the pregnancy would constitute a direct abortion and hence would be immoral; if the fetus is viable, induction would be moral if the conditions of the twofold effect are fulfilled.

Heart Conditions

Certain heart conditions at times constitute complications of pregnancy. Morally it would be forbidden to terminate a pregnancy in these cases through removal of a living nonviable fetus.

Pulmonary Tuberculosis

Pulmonary tuberculosis during pregnancy gives rise to the need for particular medical care but is, of course, not a justifying reason for therapeutic abortion. Effective means for treating the tuberculosis can be employed without doing harm to the fetus. Morally it simply is not allowed to perform a therapeutic abortion for the sake of alleviating the tuberculosis. In the case that the obstetrician believes that the mother will not be able to sustain the period of labor, Caesarian section would be justified after the fetus is viable.

Hydramnion

Hydramnion is excessive accumulation of the amniotic fluid.

If the fetus is viable, no moral problem presents itself; the membranes may be ruptured and the fluid drained off. In the rather rare case of hydramnion with a nonviable fetus, there is a dispute among moralists. In practice, the fluid may be drained off, providing there is no intention directly to take the life of the fetus.

Ectopic Gestation

Ectopic gestation is an implantation elsewhere than in the uterus, as in a fallopian tube or in the peritoneal cavity. In the vast majority of cases it is in a fallopian tube. In discussing the morality of medical procedures in these cases, certain facts should be kept in mind. There is a danger to the mother, and this arises not from the fetus as such but from the state of the tube and consequent implications of its rupture. Since the tube is in a pathologic condition, it is moral to remove it, under the principle of the twofold effect. The purpose of the procedure is to remove a pathologic organ which is a threat to the life of the mother. The death of the fetus is indirect, unintended, and merely tolerated.

Eclampsia

Eclampsia, a major toxemia of pregnancy, occurs practically always in the later stages of pregnancy. The moral principles would be the following: If competent medical advice indicates that the fetus is dead, it may be removed; if the fetus is viable and there is a proportionately grave threat to the mother, premature delivery is permissible; if the fetus is not viable (this would be rare), the pregnancy may not be terminated since this would be direct abortion.

Premature Separation of Placenta

Abruptio placentae is a premature detachment of a normally situated placenta. Placenta previa is an abnormal position of the placenta. When detachment occurs in either of these cases, hemorrhage follows. Morally the principles guiding medical procedures would be these: If medical judgment is that a viable fetus should be removed, this is moral. If there has been a complete separation of the placenta, the fetus may be removed. If there has not been a complete separation of the placenta and the fetus is still alive and nonviable, it may not be removed, even to control hemorrhage, since this would be direct abortion.

Any direct attack upon the life of a fetus for whatever cause is immoral.

Induction of Labor

Induction of labor is the act of initiating delivery of a viable fetus prior to spontaneous delivery. An *indicated induction* is an induction initiated to cure or alleviate a pathologic condition. An *elective induction* is an induction initiated in the absence of any medical indication.[4]

Determination of Viability

Determination of viability rests upon the prudent judgment of the obstetrician after due consideration of medical principles in relation to particular circumstances. It is possible, of course, that the subsequent death of the fetus may seem to show that the doctor's opinion was wrong. There is no need for trouble of conscience, however, as long as the doctor made a sincere and cautious judgment.

The direct initiation of delivery prior to viability is direct abortion and as such is a serious violation of the natural law.

The Morality of Indicated Induction

When the induction of a viable fetus is medically indicated (required for a very good medical reason), it is morally right. This moral conclusion is based upon the principle of the twofold effect. This principle spells out the conditions under which an individual may perform an act in good conscience, when the act by its nature produces both a good and a bad effect. The good effect of an indicated induction is the cure or alleviation of a pathologic con-

[4] Cf. E. Ziegel and C. Van Blarcom, *Obstetric Nursing*, 5th ed., New York: The Macmillan Company, 1964.

dition. The bad effect is the danger to the premature child. The good effect must follow from the action itself, not from the bad effect. There being no less dangerous procedure available, and the pathologic condition being of sufficient gravity to give a proper proportion between good and bad effects, it is moral to induce labor. Obviously, induction should be delayed as long as safety allows.

When the induction of a viable fetus is medically indicated, it is morally right.

The Morality of Elective Induction

For purposes of this discussion, we may divide elective induction into three conceivable kinds: harmful, risky, and harmless.

We do not presume to state whether there is truly such a thing as a harmless induction. That is a medical matter. We simply state the moral principle that would apply if there is a completely harmless elective induction. Determination of the harmlessness of an elective procedure rests upon the conscience of the physician. The presumption is in favor of nature; the burden of proof as to the harmlessness of intervention in a natural healthy process rests with the doctor.

HARMFUL ELECTIVE INDUCTION. If an elective induction will certainly harm mother or child, it is not morally allowable. The principle of the twofold effect will not apply in this case, because there is not proper proportion between human life or health and such things as convenience, money, or sentiment. A certainly harmful elective induction is bad morals and bad medicine.

RISKY ELECTIVE INDUCTION. It is not morally right to risk human life or health without a proportionately grave reason. In the absence of any pathologic condition, it is difficult to imagine a sufficiently grave reason that would allow the obstetrician to chance an induction that might harm mother or child. Such things as convenience, financial considerations, social obligations, or sentimental motives should not be weighed in the balance against a person's physical or mental well-being.

HARMLESS ELECTIVE INDUCTION. If in a particular case the

patient is at term, and the obstetrician is morally certain that induction will involve no more risk than normal delivery, such induction can be considered merely an acceleration of the natural process rather than an interference with it. This sort of elective induction would be morally allowable for a sufficient reason, even though the reason is a nonmedical one. It is not to be preferred, however, because medicine is at its best when it leaves to nature a process that is healthy, normal, and natural. All things being equal, it seems difficult to argue that intervention in a healthy natural process is as good as nonintervention.

In judging a sufficient or proportionate reason relative to these cases, the earlier the induction is initiated, the more serious the reason must be. It does not seem morally right to anticipate delivery by more than a few days.

Elective induction is morally allowable only if there is moral certitude that it involves no more risk than spontaneous delivery.

Summary

To sum up: (1) The direct initiation of delivery prior to viability is direct abortion and as such a serious violation of the natural law. (2) When induction is medically indicated, it is morally right. (3) Elective induction is morally justifiable only if there is moral certitude that it involves no more risk than normal delivery.

Euthanasia

Euthanasia is the direct killing of those who, while they have committed no crime deserving of death, are because of mental or physical defects considered of no further value to society. Euthanasia is commonly called "mercy killing." From time to time attempts are made to legalize the practice.

Arguments in Favor of Euthanasia

Proponents of euthanasia present their case through emotionally packed and appealingly presented arguments. However, when the arguments are reduced to their true substance, they come to one or several of the following:

1. You would kill a dog or horse in pain. Why not do as much for a man?
2. Why condemn a person to a life of misery?
3. Mercy killing would be painless.
4. Euthanasia relieves the family of a financial burden and an emotional strain.
5. Euthanasia often relieves society of a financial burden.

Euthanasia Is Impractical

The following reasons indicate that, entirely apart from moral considerations, it would not be expedient for society to legalize euthanasia:

1. Legalized euthanasia would lessen the incentive for medical research.
2. It would become possible to arrange for the death of an enemy or a wealthy relative.
3. Voluntary euthanasia is but a step removed from compulsory euthanasia.
4. The purpose of the medical profession is to preserve life, not to destroy it.
5. Many patients today surprise the doctor by recovering. Under legalized euthanasia, they would be killed.
6. The practice of euthanasia would make the doctor a man from whom we would wish to flee in terror when seriously ill.

Euthanasia Is Immoral

As impractical and harmful as the legalization of euthanasia would be, the basic reason for rejecting it is a moral one. Euthanasia is a bold and outrageous infringement upon the sovereign rights of Almighty God. God alone, as our Creator, has dominion over life. Our life is to end when God so wills and not before. When a man dares to terminate a human life, he is guilty of serious immorality. Such misconduct cannot be made right by the passage of any sort of legislation by any authority on earth.

Medical Association Condemns Euthanasia

In 1950, the World Medical Association, of which the American Medical Association is a member, condemned euthanasia with these words: "The council of the World Medical Association believes that the practice of euthanasia is contrary to the public interest and to medical ethical principles as well as to natural rights."

Administration of Narcotics to the Dying

It is a frequent practice to give narcotics when death is approaching. Providing certain conditions are fulfilled, this is morally justified.

The administration of narcotics to the dying is morally justified if the following three conditions are fulfilled: (1) The opportunity for receiving the sacraments has been given (in the case of a Catholic patient); (2) there is severe physical pain to be relieved; and (3) the dose is not lethal.

Commenting on this subject, Pope Pius XII laid down very concrete norms. In an address delivered to a symposium on anesthesiology, the Holy Father asked three questions:

1. Is there a universal moral obligation to refuse analgesia and to accept physical pain in the spirit of faith?

2. Is it in accord with the spirit of the Gospel to bring about by means of drugs the loss of consciousness and of the use of a man's higher faculties?

3. Is it lawful for the dying or those in danger of death to make use of drugs even if the lessening of pain is probably accompanied by a shortening of life?

Essentially the Holy Father gave the answer "No" to the first question and "Yes" to the second and third. We have extracted from his discourse a few important observations:

The patient desirous of avoiding or lessening pain can in good conscience make use of the means discovered by science which in themselves are not immoral. The Christian's duty of renunciation and of interior purification is not an obstacle to the use of anesthetics. Narcosis involving a lessening or a suppression of consciousness is permitted by natural morality and is in keeping with the spirit of the Gospel. If the dying man has fulfilled all his duties and received the last sacraments, if medical reasons clearly suggest the use of anesthetics, if in determining the dose the permitted amount is not exceeded, if the intensity and duration of this treatment is carefully calculated and the patient consents to it, then there is no objection. The use of anesthetics is morally permissible.

All forms of direct euthanasia, that is, the administration of a drug in order to produce or hasten death, are unlawful, because in that case one asserts the right to dispose directly of life.

If there exists no direct causal link, either through the will of the interested parties or by the nature of things, between the induced unconsciousness and the shortening of life (as would be the case if the suppression of the pain could be obtained only by the shortening of life); and if, on the other hand, the actual administration of drugs brings about two distinct effects, one the relief of pain and the other the shortening of life, the action is lawful.[5]

To deprive the patient of his consciousness before he has had the opportunity to confess his sins and to receive the sacraments devoutly is, at best, to deprive him of much spiritual merit and, at worst, to take away his last chance of salvation.

It is not morally right to administer narcotics to the dying to relieve mental stress. If there is no severe physical pain, the patient

[5] Pope Pius XII, address to a symposium on anesthesiology, February 24, 1957. Extracts.

should be left conscious as long as God does not take his consciousness away.

The administration of a lethal dose to a patient is murder. Usually the nurse is morally blameless if she follows the doctor's orders. However, if he prescribes a dose that is obviously lethal, the nurse should refuse to execute the order.

When an extremely weak patient has excruciating pain, narcotics may be administered even though there is a danger of shortening his life. This is permissible by application of the principle of the twofold effect, because the reason for the administration of such medication is to relieve pain not to cause death.

Topics for Discussion

Items may be true, partly true, erroneous, or unsolvable. First judge, then discuss.

1. Investigate the legal aspects of abortion in your locality and compare them with your moral principles.
2. An obstetrician is scheduled to give an important address to a medical convention. In order to arrive on time, he induces his patient.
3. Does the Catholic Church teach that the life of the child is to be preferred over that of the mother?
4. A doctor works in an infertility clinic in a Catholic hospital one day a week. The rest of the week he works in a birth control clinic. The administrator of the Catholic hospital discovers this and withdraws his privileges. Is this justified?

Cases for Solution

1. A pregnant woman is in critical need of an appendectomy. This may result in an abortion. May she undergo the operation?
2. A pregnant woman is hemorrhaging. Is it moral to prescribe a drug that will stop the hemorrhage and probably cause an abortion?
3. A patient with terminal cancer requests that any further efforts to prolong his life be discontinued. As long as nothing is done to directly kill him, is it moral to discontinue all efforts to keep him alive?

References for Further Study

Bouscaren, T. *Ethics of Ectopic Operations,* Milwaukee: Bruce Publishing Company, 1944.

Finney, Patrick, and O'Brien, Patrick. *Moral Problems in Hospital Practice,* St. Louis: B. Herder Book Co., 1956.

Godin, Edgar, and O'Hanley, J. P. E. *Hospital Ethics,* Bathurst, New Brunswick, Canada: Hotel Dieu Hospital, 1957.

Kelley, Gerard. *Medico-Moral Problems,* St. Louis: The Catholic Hospital Association of America and Canada, 1959.

Kenny, John P. *Principles of Medical Ethics,* Westminster, Md.: The Newman Press, 1962.

McFadden, C. J. *Medical Ethics,* 5th ed., Philadelphia: F. A. Davis Company, 1961.

Marshall, John. *The Ethics of Medical Practice,* London: Darton, Longman and Todd, 1960.

Niedermeyer, Albert. *Compendium of Pastoral Medicine,* New York: Joseph F. Wagner, Inc., 1961. (Trans. by Fulgence Buonanno.)

O'Donnell, Thomas J. *Morals in Medicine,* Westminster, Md.: The Newman Press, 1956.

Sullivan, J. *The Morality of Mercy Killing,* Westminster, Md.: The Newman Press, 1950.

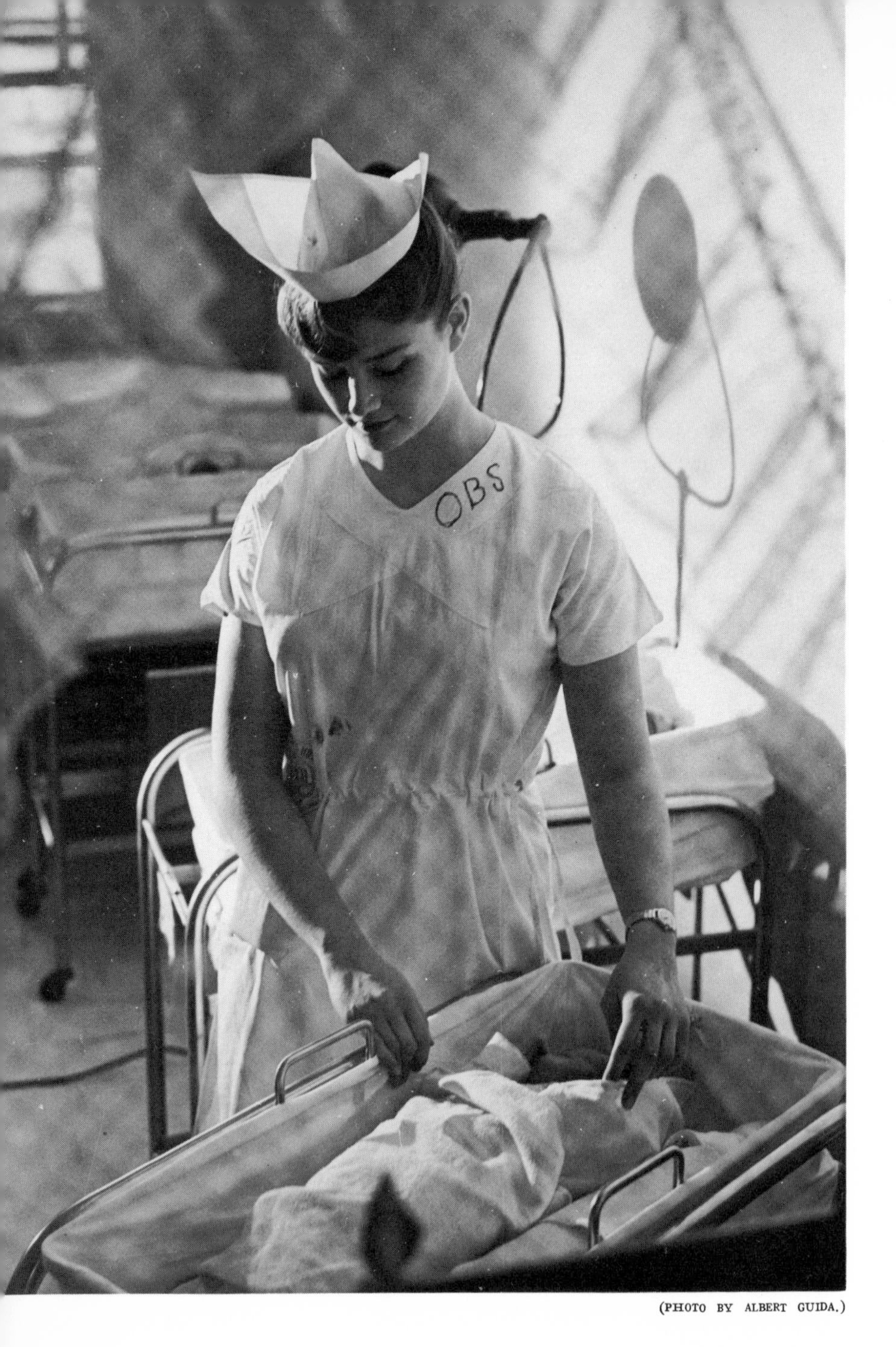

(PHOTO BY ALBERT GUIDA.)

St. Vincent's Hospital, New York.

CHAPTER 9

Principles Relating to the Preservation of Life

Mutilation · Excision · Sterilization · Plastic surgery · Tissue transplantation · Neuropsychiatric procedures · Alcoholism · Drug addiction · Practical points regarding cooperation · Disaster nursing

Mutilation

Mutilation is any lessening of the integrity of the human body. This definition embraces the term in its broadest aspect and is therefore completely comprehensive. Included under it are such widely divergent procedures as tooth extraction, blood donation, circumcision, and amputation.

A major mutilation is anything which of its very nature renders the individual unfit for natural functions or, in other words, destroys his functional integrity, for example, sterilization, laryngectomy, glossectomy. Theologically, this sort of mutilation would be called "mutilation in the strict sense."

A minor mutilation is any lessening of the sum total of the body which does not destroy its functional integrity, for example, tonsillectomy, salpingectomy, rib resection. The theological term to describe this sort of mutilation would be "mutilation in a broad sense."

Morally, therefore, a distinction may be made between two

types of mutilation. This distinction is based upon the concept of the functional integrity of the human body. By functional integrity is meant the degree of completeness necessary for the performance of the functions proper to the body. For example, functional integrity would be destroyed by the amputation of a leg; but the removal of one of two normal kidneys would still leave the degree of completeness necessary for the performance of kidney function.

When a mutilation is necessary for the preservation of the life or health of one's body, it is performed upon the presumed permission of Almighty God, the Supreme Lord of every human being. We shall discuss detailed application of this principle in the sections following, speaking first of the excision of pathologic organs, which is moral, and then of the excision of healthy organs, which is sometimes moral but usually immoral. We shall discuss the application of our principles to particular cases, such as sterilization, ectopic pregnancies, destruction of fetal life, and plastic surgery.

A relatively recent medical procedure involves the donation of part of one's body to another person to preserve his life or health, such as has been done in cases of kidney transplantation from twin to twin, and from brother to sister. This we shall discuss under the heading of "Tissue Transplantation."

Excision

Excision of Pathologic Organs Is Moral

Removal of pathologic organs to save the entire body is permissible by natural law. Since the whole is greater than any of its parts, common sense dictates that the removal of a diseased organ is permissible for the good of the whole body when it cannot be secured by other means. For example, occasionally it becomes necessary to amputate a gangrenous leg so that the life of the patient may be saved. This is an application of the principle of totality.

Excision of Nonpathologic Organs Is Sometimes Moral

Surgical removal of a healthy organ from the human body *to cure or arrest the further development of disease in another organ* may be allowed in certain well-defined cases. Two conditions must exist. First, the preservation or continued functioning of a particular organ must cause serious harm or constitute a threat to the whole body. Second, it must be known that such harm cannot be avoided, or at least notably diminished, except by a mutilation—and the effectiveness of the mutilation must be well established.

The decisive point is not that the organ removed or rendered inoperative is itself diseased, but that its preservation and functioning constitute a serious threat for the whole body. For example, in the case of cancer of the breast, it is permissible to perform an oophorectomy in spite of the fact that the ovaries are healthy, because the normal functioning of the ovaries fosters the growth of the cancer. Likewise, in the case of cancer of the prostate, an orchidectomy is permissible.

This conclusion is deduced from the custodial rights over his body which an individual receives from the Creator and is in accordance with the *principle of totality*, which teaches that *every particular organ is subject to the organic whole of the body and must submit to it in case of conflict.* This is why surgical removal of a nonpathologic organ to cure or correct disease in another organ is a moral procedure when the requisite conditions are fulfilled.

Another justifying cause for the removal of an apparently healthy organ would be the *probability of latent or incipient pathology* in the average person. If the mutilation is a minor one, and a reasonable cause exists for the excision, it would be moral to remove the organ. For example, a normal appendix could be removed during a cholecystectomy. This is allowed on the grounds of probability of latent or incipient appendicitis in the average person. So, too, a man going to a place where proper medical care would be difficult to obtain could have his apparently healthy appendix removed beforehand. A trapper about to leave for a prolonged stay in the Canadian wilderness would be justified in taking such a precaution.

Removal of a normal appendix or tonsil is never justified without sufficient reason for exposing the person to the risks involved in an operation. A nurse asked to assist in such a procedure would normally presume a sufficient reason.

Some physicians perform an elective circumcision routinely on male infants. The reason often given for this is potential phimosis. Other doctors do not agree with this custom and maintain that circumcision should not be performed without a medical indication. The arguments in favor of elective circumcision seem rather weak. It would, however, be morally permissible for a nurse to assist at the procedure.

Excision of Nonpathologic Organs Is Usually Immoral

Keeping in mind the exceptions we have just explained, we may state the general principle regarding the excision of nonpathologic organs: *The removal of healthy organs is usually immoral.* Therefore, the nurse cannot ordinarily assist at such procedures with clear conscience. The usual direct sterilization would be a case in point.

Bone Bank

There is no moral objection to the bone bank.

Autopsy

Given the consent of the competent relative or the order of civil authority, there is no moral objection to autopsy.

Disposal of Amputated or Excised Parts

There is an obligation to bury amputated limbs, as long as there is no considerable inconvenience involved. The nurse may cooperate ordinarily with clear conscience in the usual procedure of the institution where she is employed.

Sterilization

Sterility is the inability to reproduce. This should not be confused with impotency, which is the impossibility of performing the marriage act.

There is a vast and essential moral difference between direct sterilization and indirect sterilization. *Direct sterilization is that which has as its immediate purpose the making of reproduction impossible.* This is a very serious mutilation, contrary to the natural law, and is always immoral. Under this heading fall hysterectomy, ligation of fallopian tubes, ligation of vas deferens, oophorectomy, salpingectomy, and radiation with x-ray, when done solely for the purpose of sterilizing. On the other hand, at times in order to save the health of an individual, it may be necessary to perform an operation which results in sterility. This is licit by the principle of the twofold effect. *Indirect sterilization is that which occurs as a necessary and unintended consequence of a medical procedure which has for its purpose the cure or removal of a pathologic organ.* Such a thing may happen, for instance, in the case of a bilateral salpingectomy for hydrosalpinx. *Indirect sterilization is always moral; direct sterilization is always immoral.* This is the essential distinction to keep in mind regarding the morality of sterilization.

We sometimes hear the term *therapeutic sterilization*, which is sterilization for purposes of cure. This is moral if indirect, that is, if a pathologic condition exists and the operation is performed to save the life or health of the individual concerned. If, however, the so-called therapeutic sterilization is performed to avoid some real or imaginary future illness, it is a direct sterilization and therefore immoral. For example, it is often proposed to sterilize a woman who has no disorder but whose next delivery is expected to be quite difficult. Such a procedure would not be moral, because the principle of the twofold effect does not apply.

Ligation of the fallopian tubes or of the vas deferens, having as its purpose the avoidance of conception, is immoral. The immorality flows not only from the contraceptive intent but also from the fact that an unjustified mutilation is performed.[1]

When we consider other means of sterilization, however it is necessary to make distinctions. Vasectomy, orchidectomy, oophorectomy, salpingectomy, and hysterectomy are sterilizing operations. But such excisions are frequently performed to remove a diseased organ. Here we must apply the principle of the twofold effect, whereby the excision is allowable because the sterilization only occurs as a concomitant effect of the good action which is performed to eliminate a pathologic condition. In other words, if the operation is performed for the purpose of sterilizing the patient (direct sterilization), it is immoral; but if it is performed to cure or remove a pathologic organ (indirect sterilization), it is moral.

It is also moral to remove a healthy organ to save the entire body. If the removal of the ovaries will retard breast cancer, this can be done morally. The principle of totality applies in this case. One organ must be sacrificed for the good of the whole body.

Punitive sterilization is the sterilizing of a criminal as a punishment, especially for sex crimes. This is little or no punishment, in reality. The operation, in the case of the male, is minor; and the effect is to make further sex acts "safe," since conception is impossible. The morality of such sterilization is under dispute, but we hold that it is immoral.

Eugenic sterilization is the sterilizing of those who are expected to have defective children. This is immoral because no authority has such power over the bodies of human beings. Moreover, competent experts on the subject maintain that this sort of sterilization would have no appreciable effect in improving the human race.

[1] Cf. John Marshall, *The Ethics of Medical Practice*, London: Darton, Longman & Todd, 1960, p. 63.

Plastic Surgery

Plastic surgery is surgery which aims to repair or restore (chiefly by tissue transfer) parts of the body that have been lost, injured, or deformed.

Plastic surgery is clearly a form of mutilation and as such is governed by the general rules of mutilation. There are, however, some specific moral aspects relative to plastic surgery about which the nurse should be familiar.

There are, in general, three circumstances in which plastic surgery would be employed: to remedy what might truly be called a physical pathologic state (e.g., a skin graft that is necessary after an operation on a tubercular bone in a patient's leg); to change one's physical appearance or enhance beauty; or for psychological considerations.

If plastic surgery is clearly indicated for medical reasons, as in the case mentioned concerning a skin graft after an operation on a tubercular bone, there is no moral problem.

In the case of the change of one's physical appearance, purpose and circumstance must determine the morality. If there are proper safeguards relative to the life and health of the subject, if there is a reason sufficiently grave in proportion to the seriousness of the operation, and if the purpose is good, then plastic surgery may be performed in good conscience. A teacher, otherwise highly gifted, finds that her unpleasant facial characteristics are detrimental to her work. She would be justified in taking steps to have the defect corrected.

Relative to psychological consideration, if a feeling of inferiority, a complex, or neurosis could be remedied by plastic surgery, this would not only be morally allowed but also advisable.

Pope Pius XII has concisely summed up the moral and spiritual implication of plastic surgery in these words:

> Christian morality, that looks toward man's ultimate end and embraces and regulates the totality of human values, cannot but assign to physical beauty the place which belongs to it—and that is certainly not

at the top of the scale of values, since it is neither a spiritual nor an essential good. When the modern development of esthetic surgery seeks the opinion of Christian morals, it does nothing more than ask where in the scale of values physical beauty should be placed.

The morality of actions that are involved in esthetic surgery depends on the concrete circumstances of individual cases. In the moral evaluation of these circumstances, the principal conditions most pertinent to the matter and most determinative in the vast study of cases presented by esthetic surgery are the following: that the intention be good, that the general health of the subject be protected from notable risks, and that the motives be reasonable and proportionate to the "extraordinary means" to which recourse is taken.

Obvious, for example, is the illicitness of an operation sought with the intention of increasing one's own power of seduction and thus inducing others more easily into sin; or exclusively to wrest a guilty person from justice; or an operation damaging to the regular functions of the physical organs; or one desired only through mere vanity or the whims of fashion.

On the other hand, there are many reasons why an operation might be legitimate, and even at times advisable.

Some disfigurements, or perhaps mere imperfections, are causes of psychic disturbances in a patient, or can become an obstacle in social and family relations; or an impediment—particularly in people devoted to public life or art—in the development of their careers.

Although the duty to help these patients may belong to many—priests, psychiatrists, friends—when the cause consists of a physical defect which plastic surgery is capable of removing to some degree, no one can deny that a surgical operation is not only medically and esthetically advisable, but is also indicated for spiritual reasons.[2]

Tissue Transplantation

Tissue transplantation is the transfer of any organized living matter. Examples of this are blood donation and corneal transplantation. In discussing tissue transplantation in its broader aspects, we may include also the use of tissue derivatives, such as insulin and testosterone. (See Figs. 12*A* and 12*B*, pp. 144, 145.)

Transplantation may be grouped generally under three headings: autograft, homograft, and heterograft.

[2] Pope Pius XII, address delivered to members of the Italian Association of Plastic Surgeons, October 4, 1958. Extracts.

Autograft is the transplantation of one's own tissue, such as skin graft. It presents no moral problem.

Homograft is the transplantation of tissue from one human body to another. Homograft *from the dead* presents no moral problem. Corneal transplantation from the recent dead is an example. Preservation of tissue for future use ("bone bank," "vascular bank") is morally permissible.

Homograft *from the living* (from man to man) may be termed "tissue donation." Any procedure of this nature involves mutilation. If the mutilation does not destroy the functional integrity of the donor, it is morally permissible according to good opinion. Examples are blood donation and kidney transplantation. If the mutilation destroys the functional integrity of the donor, it is immoral. An example would be the donation of both corneas.

Heterograft is the use of tissue or tissue derivatives from a different species (animal to man). The use of tissue derivatives presents no moral problems. Examples would be liver extract and estrogen.

The use of animal tissue, if biologically possible, would be permissible. Sex glands would be an exception because the generative functions of man are of an entirely different order from those of animals, involving as they do the procreation not merely of an animal body but of a human being, whose body is united to an immortal soul.

The nurse will be guided in her assistance in tissue transplantation by the application of the principles we have enumerated in the light of the ordinary moral principles of cooperation.

Neuropsychiatric Procedures

Hypnosis

Hypnosis is an artificially induced state resembling sleep, which is characterized by a particular type of rapport between subject and operator, in which the subject's awareness is narrowed and suggestibility is heightened.

The word "hypnosis" comes from a Greek word meaning

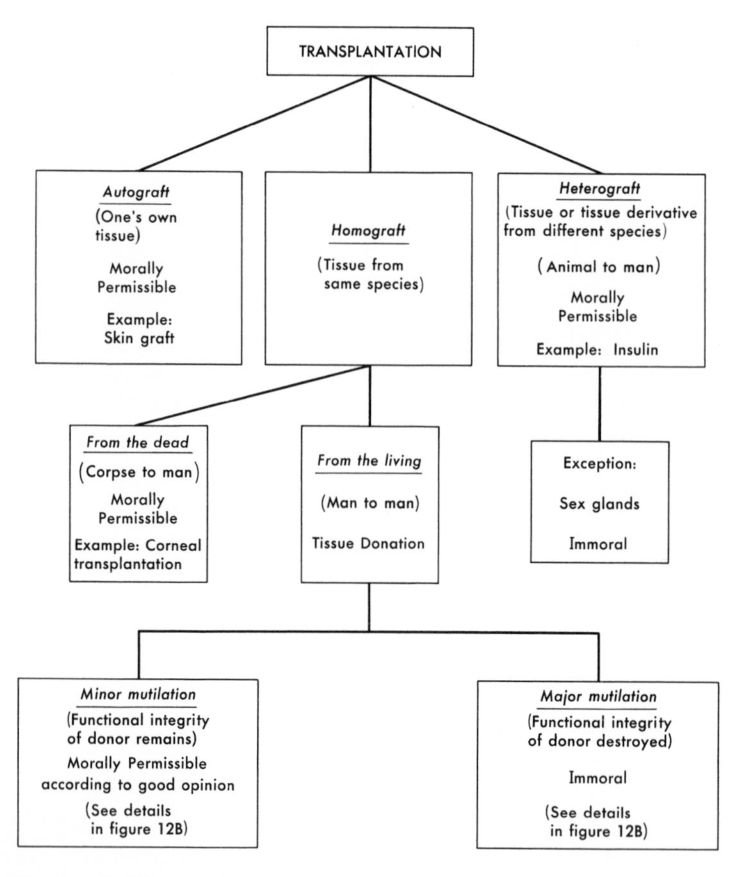

Figure 12A. The morality of transplantation of tissue and tissue derivatives.

"sleep." A hypnotic sleep can be induced by various methods. The operator is known as a hypnotist. Apparently hypnosis was used from very early times, but its formal acceptance as an adjunct to the medical profession is recent.

The exact nature of hypnosis is not known. Various theories which have been proposed to explain it are quite unconvincing.

A rather small minority of people apparently cannot be hypnotized. A keen imagination seems to heighten susceptibility. Children between seven and fourteen seem to be most susceptible, while elderly people are least susceptible. There is no proof that sex is a

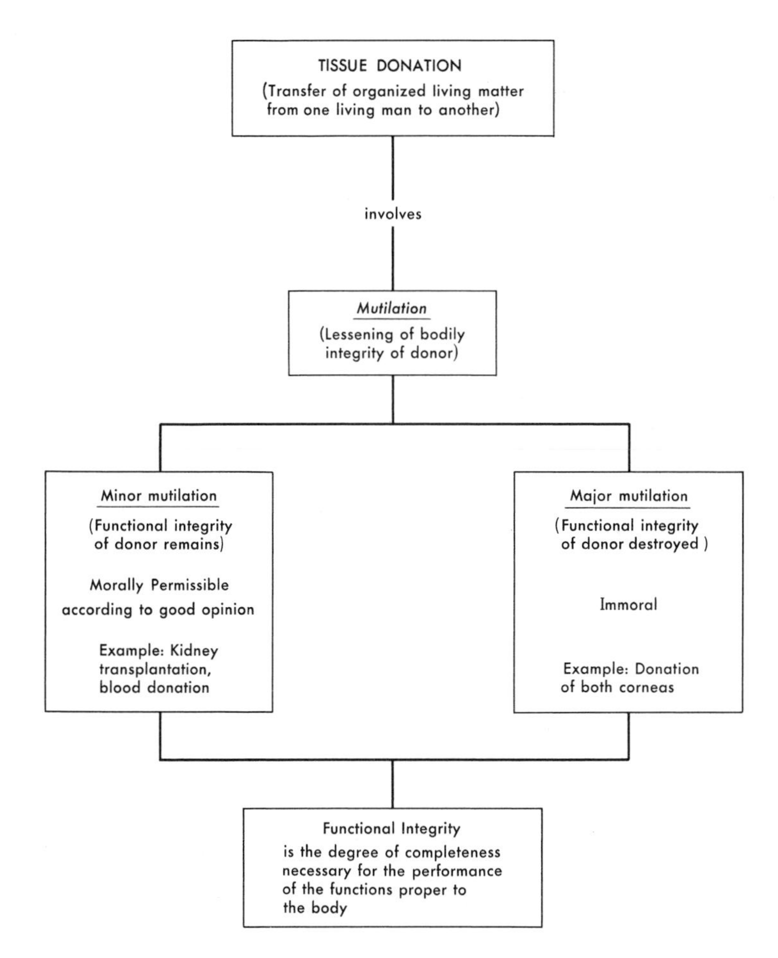

Figure 12B. The morality of tissue donation.

factor. Psychotics can be hypnotized, although good results are questionable. Lack of voluntary cooperation is not necessarily an impediment to hypnosis.

Dehypnotization offers no serious problems. An occasional subject who does not awaken upon the command of the hypnotist will awaken spontaneously at another time.

A posthypnotic suggestion is one made by the hypnotist to the subject while in the hypnotic state to be carried out later. Certain subjects are very suggestible. Obviously this power of the hypnotist carries with it both good and evil potentialities. In practice, the question "What is hypnotism?" is much less important than the question "Who is the hypnotist?"

Hypnosis has been found useful in psychiatry, anesthesia, dentistry, obstetrics, gynecology, treatment of asthma, migraine headaches, nervous tics, and in connection with pain relief. Its use as entertainment is morally wrong.

Hypnosis can be used in good conscience when certain conditions are fulfilled:

1. A grave reason must exist.
2. The subject's permission should be obtained.
3. The possibility of using less radical means must be absent.
4. Those conducting the procedure should be of good moral character.
5. Those conducting the procedure must have proper training and sufficient skill.

Hypnosis in the absence of a witness would not in itself offend good morals. However, the presence of a witness is dictated by prudence and is therefore a very strong recommendation.

> The use of hypnosis for fun or as a gag is a travesty on human dignity. Hypnosis is not a toy for amateurs to play with. It makes as much sense to use hypnosis for fun as it does to use opiates or other drugs for similar purpose. It can only result in great harm with possible breakdown in individual defenses and end in intense anxiety or hysteria. In untrained hands, hypnosis may do irreparable damage.[3]

Cordotomy

A cordotomy is moral when performed to relieve extreme pain in an incurable patient who has built up a tolerance to the ordinary forms of relief. The principle of totality applies.

[3] Milton J. Marmer, *Hypnosis in Anesthesiology*, Springfield, Ill.: Charles C Thomas, 1959, pp. 116-17.

Prefrontal Lobotomy

In mental therapy, prefrontal lobotomy presents a special problem in cooperation, because sometimes it is moral and sometimes it is not. It is moral when it is used as a last resort in attempting to aid a patient suffering from serious mental illness. On the other hand, it is immoral when less extreme measures are available, or when the probability of harm outweighs the probability of benefit. The nurse can presume that a cordotomy or a prefrontal lobotomy is moral as long as the opposite is not certain.

Lie-Detector Tests

Lie-detector tests are based upon the fact that in most cases the mental tension of a liar gives rise to concomitant and measurable physical reactions. Under emotional stress, the adrenal glands produce epinephrine (Adrenalin) in increased amounts. This causes immediate but transitory reactions: the blood vessels contract, raising the blood pressure sharply; the heart rate increases; muscles contract, causing the skin to become taut; respirations become rapid and labored.[4] Since these symptoms disappear quickly, their relationship to a series of questions can be recorded graphically. This is accomplished by means of electronic detectors which record the various impulses on a moving tape. The result is a graph which can be read and studied by an expert examiner. In general, the process resembles an electrocardiogram.

When a lie-detector test is being given, the operator marks the graph to correlate each question with the concomitant physical reactions. A series of test questions establishes the general pattern of the subject's reactions. Questions are so framed that the answers are simply positive or negative.

There is no moral problem connected with the taking of such

[4] Cf. H. Wright and M. Montag, *Materia Medica, Pharmacology and Therapeutics*, 7th ed., Philadelphia: W. B. Saunders Company, 1959.

measurements, and therefore when the subject consents, a lie-detector test may be used without sin.

We might ask whether it is morally right to oblige an individual to undergo a lie-detector test. Generally speaking, the answer is "No." A man is not obliged by moral law to be a witness against himself, or to turn himself over to authority for punishment. Undergoing a lie-detector test would be equivalent to so doing. Therefore ordinarily one would not be morally bound to submit to such a test, nor would authority be right in forcing such a test upon an individual. Under the natural law, if our refusal would bring grave harm to a third party or to the common good, we might be obliged to undergo the test. However, we are permitted by moral law to take advantage of legal safeguards offered us by civil law. A lie-detector test would be used only in connection with civil procedure. Civil law imposing no such requirement, the moral obligation of submitting to a lie-detector test would not in practice be incumbent upon an individual.

Amobarbital (Amytal Sodium)

Regarding so-called truth serum, let it be mentioned immediately that this drug does not furnish, as it were, a master key to everything in a person's mind, as many people believe. It does not break down the subject's will to conceal his thoughts. Rather it breaks through his inhibitions, making it easier for him to reveal what he is thinking. Just how much is revealed depends on the docility of the subject. Some subjects, when given the "truth serum" treatment, show no effect beyond what has all the appearances of a state of inebriation.

The drug popularly described as "truth serum" is amobarbital sodium (Amytal Sodium), a short-acting, central nervous system depressant. It produces a sleep from which the subject can be roused sufficiently to answer questions.[5] In some cases, the answers prove to be of help in discovering the source of mental disturbance. Amobarbital was used extensively in the treatment of war neuroses

[5] Wright and Montag, *op. cit.*, p. 168.

in World War II. In many cases, the answers prove to be absolutely useless. Some subjects flatly refuse to give answers. The employment of amobarbital to extract the truth from hardened criminals constitutes good material for cheap novels but has no practical value.

Amobarbital can be used in good conscience for the purpose of eliciting information when certain conditions are fulfilled: (1) A grave reason must exist. (2) The subject's permission should be obtained. (3) The possibility of using other less radical means must be absent. (4) A competent physician must be constantly in attendance. (5) A witness should be present. (6) Those administering the treatment should be of good moral character. These conditions are fundamentally the same as those which apply to hypnotism.

Alcoholism

The abuse of alcohol involves a threefold consideration: physical, mental, and spiritual. It is a mistake to ignore any of these three aspects of the problem, because an effective solution depends on an adjustment of a personality on all three levels.

Let us not fall victim to the modern error that drunkards are merely sick and are therefore not responsible for their condition and not capable of stopping their evil practices. If all drunkards are nothing else but the innocent victims of an unpleasant disease, how can the Bible threaten them with hell? "It is not . . . the drunkards . . . that will inherit the kingdom of God" (I Cor. 6:10).

Certainly we should be charitable to drunkards. But to hold them all blameless is not charity. Such an attitude merely furnishes them with an excuse and lessens their chances of a cure. Every victim of drink, whether physically ill or just plain morally bad, must contribute to his own recovery by the exercise of his God-given faculty of free will, unless (in a rare case) he is so physically impelled toward liquor that he no longer retains the use of reason and free will. It is the place of the nurse to assist him in strengthening his will, as well as in curing any physical ailment he might have.

The famous organization known as Alcoholics Anonymous has enjoyed notable success in working with this problem. Their "Twelve Steps" are worthy of consideration:

1. We admitted we were powerless over alcohol—that our lives had become unmanageable.
2. Came to believe that a Power greater than ourselves could restore us to sanity.
3. Made a decision to turn our will and our lives over to the care of God as we understood Him.
4. Made a searching and fearless moral inventory of ourselves.
5. Admitted to God, to ourselves, and to another human being the exact nature of our wrongs.
6. Were entirely ready to have God remove all these defects of character.
7. Humbly asked Him to remove our shortcomings.
8. Made a list of all persons we had harmed and became willing to make amends to them all.
9. Made direct amends to such people wherever possible, except when to do so would injure them or others.
10. Continued to take personal inventory and when we were wrong promptly admitted it.
11. Sought through prayer and meditation to improve our conscious contact with God as we understood Him, praying only for knowledge of His will for us and the power to carry that out.
12. Having had a spiritual awakening as a result of these steps, we tried to carry this message to alcoholics, and to practice these principles in all our affairs.

Drug Addiction

Drug addiction, like alcoholism, involves a threefold consideration: physical, mental, and spiritual. In this case, the physical and mental aspects are ordinarily recognized, but the spiritual is frequently ignored.

In light of the crisis that drug addiction brings to a human life, the need for spiritual assistance should never be minimized.

The prudent nurse needs no warning regarding the danger of self-addiction. Those engaged in the handling of narcotics and barbiturates may be at times strongly tempted. *Principiis obsta*—"Oppose the beginnings."

Practical Points Regarding Cooperation

Walking off a Case

It sometimes happens that a nurse will start a case in good faith, and during the operation the surgeon surprises her by beginning an immoral procedure. If another nurse is available to take over rather quickly, the Catholic nurse should state her attitude and leave the room. However, if there is no substitute available, she should protest to the doctor but remain on the case, because to leave might endanger the life of the patient.

Once a nurse knows that a certain doctor has a custom of performing immoral operations after having booked the case under an innocent title, she should refuse to scrub for him at all, until such time as he changes his deceptive mode of conduct.

Securing a Position in a Non-Catholic Institution

When a Catholic nurse applies for a position in a non-Catholic institution, she should make her stand clear that she will not assist at immoral operations or at operations to which she would have conscientious objections. Most hospitals will honor this request.

Disaster Nursing

Hardly a day goes by without our reading of tragedy in the form of auto accidents, plane crashes, and train wrecks or of accidental drownings or injuries caused by storms, floods, and civil uprisings. Nurses the world over constantly find themselves in positions where they must practice their profession in sudden and unusual circumstances.

Disaster, whether on a national or local level, whether caused by nature or man, may strike at any time. The nurse, as a citizen of her community and a member of a profession serving humanity, should know what plans have been made for emergency situations in her locality, and where she as an individual fits into the plan.

She could enroll in advanced first aid courses or disaster survival courses, which are available in almost all communities, or use her professional training to teach courses to laymen. Married nurses should have a plan for the temporary care of their children so that they might assist the community in time of need.

If disaster strikes, the nurse who is employed by a hospital should report for duty as quickly as possible and follow its emergency plan. However, if she is unable to reach her post, as might happen in a severe storm or flood, she could report to a local medical aid center and assist with the care of casualties. In the United States the Office of Civil Defense and Disaster Control has set up areas in all communities for this purpose.

In the absence of physicians, nurses would be expected to care for the sick and the injured and to supervise and teach nonprofessional people in the care of the injured.

Perhaps the most difficult task for the nurse in a serious disaster would be the adjustment to the rule that those with the less serious injury must be treated first, so that they may return to a useful life as quickly as possible; and those most seriously injured should receive only minimal care, such as the control of obvious hemorrhage and maintenance of an open airway.

In the above situation, no moral principles are violated because in the absence of trained medical personnel and adequate equipment *the greatest good must be done for the greatest number.*

The Catholic nurse, in all situations, must remember her duty to see to the spiritual care of her charges; baptizing the aborted fetus or the sickly newborn, assisting the dying to make their most important Act of Contrition, and encouraging all about her to trust in the providence of Almighty God.

Topics for Discussion

Items may be true, partly true, erroneous, or unsolvable. First judge, then discuss.

1. A nurse, out of a sense of pity, gives alcohol to an alcoholic patient without an order. She is convinced that this is the best way under the circumstances to alleviate his suffering and ultimately effect a cure.
2. A woman prisoner of war fears attack upon her virtue. In order to prevent this, she deliberately disfigures her face. Is such a self-mutilation justified?
3. It is the common practice in the United States to circumcise infants. In many other countries, this is only done in the presence of an indication. Discuss this situation in the light of the principles of mutilation.

Cases for Solution

1. A patient with an ectopic gestation is cured by the usual removal of the affected fallopian tube. Two years later, she is admitted with ovarian cancer on the opposite side. Removal of the diseased ovary will sterilize the patient. Is the procedure moral?
2. A young nurse has a nose of unusual size and as a result is the butt of unkind remarks. A doctor who is a friend of hers offers to perform plastic surgery to correct the defect, but another nurse says she thinks it would be wrong because vanity is the motive.
3. A man in drawing up his will wishes to donate his corneas to an eye bank, but his lawyer expresses the opinion that although such a thing would be legal, it may not be moral.

References for Further Study

Connell, F. J. *Father Connell Answers Moral Questions,* Washington, D.C.: Catholic University of America Press, 1959.

Godin, Edgar, and O'Hanley, J. P. E. *Hospital Ethics,* Bathurst, New Brunswick, Canada: Hotel Dieu Hospital, 1957.

Healy, E. F. *Medical Ethics,* Chicago: Loyola University Press, 1956.

Kenny, John P. *Principles of Medical Ethics,* Westminster, Md.: The Newman Press, 1962.

Magonet, A. P. *Hypnosis in Medicine,* London: William Heinermann Medical Books, Ltd., 1952.

Marmer, M. J. *Hypnosis in Anesthesiology,* Springfield, Ill.: Charles C Thomas, 1959.

Marshall, John. *The Ethics of Medical Practice,* London: Darton, Longman and Todd, 1960.

Niedermeyer, Albert. *Compendium of Pastoral Medicine,* New York: Joseph F. Wagner, Inc., 1961. (Trans. by Fulgence Buonanno.)

Shinners, J. *The Morality of Medical Experimentation on Living Human Subjects in the Light of Recent Papal Pronouncements,* Washington, D.C.: The Catholic University of America Press, 1958.

THERE ARE SOME WHO CAN RISE TO GREAT HEIGHTS NOW AND THEN IN EXTRAORDINARY CIRCUMSTANCES, BUT WHO TIRE AND ARE IRRITATED BY THE CONSTANT SMALL BOTHERS WHICH OCCUR DAY IN AND DAY OUT.

PIUS XII

Address to the nursing staff of Roman institutions, May 21, 1952.

PART III

Responsibilities of the Nurse to Her Patient

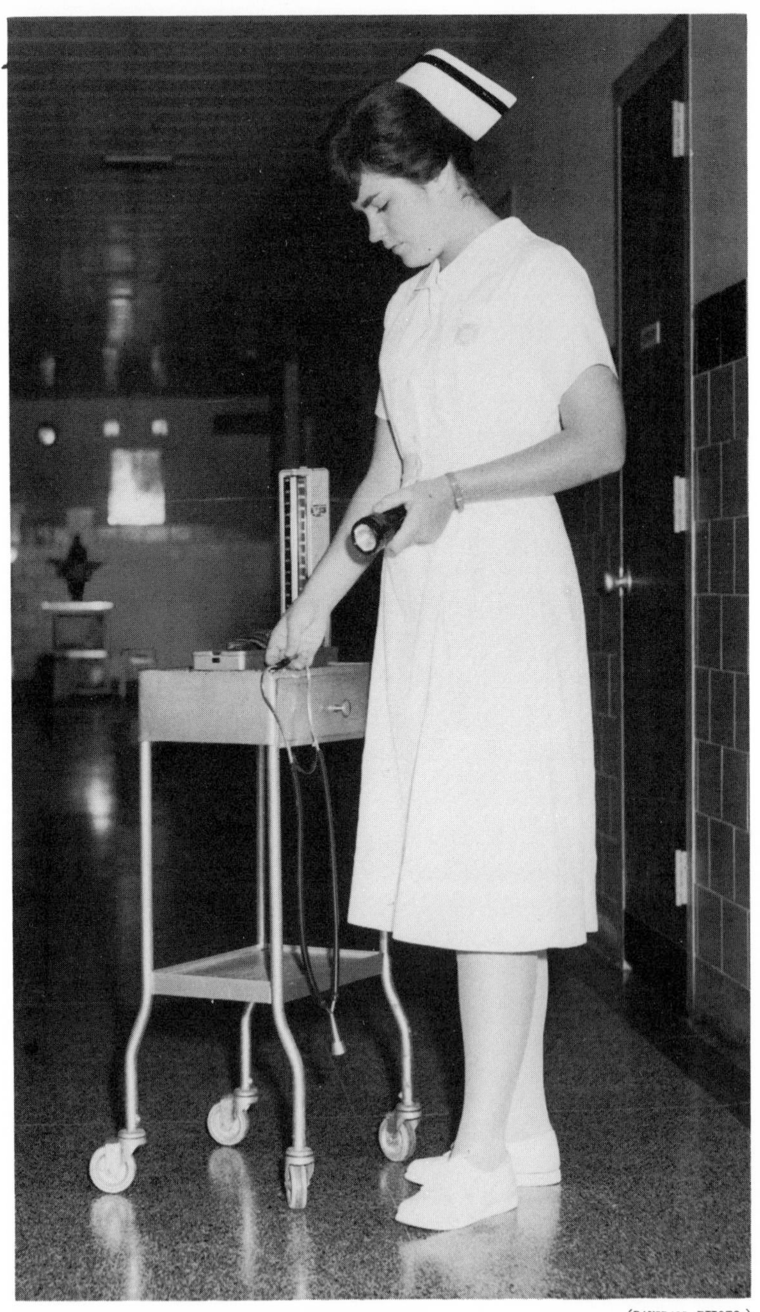

(DAVIDAN PHOTO.)

Holy Name Hospital, Teaneck, New Jersey.

CHAPTER 10

The Rights of the Patient

The virtue of justice · Professional secrecy · Truthfulness · Disclosure of medical information · The patient as an individual

The Virtue of Justice

Care of Property

The nurse faces a twofold responsibility regarding the care of properties: care of the property of the patient and care of the property of the institution.

A special temptation to theft is present in both of these cases. In the first place, the patient is often in no position to protect his property rights, due either to the use of narcotics or to his general debility. Second, there is a general opinion prevalent that thefts from institutions are excusable.

Theft from an institution can be as serious as theft from an individual. It is possible to commit a grave sin in both instances. Any opinion to the contrary is definitely erroneous.

In regard to the patient, the fact that he is in a helpless condition, while it offers a special temptation of theft, at the same time increases the malice of any theft that may be committed.

It is the duty of the nurse to take conscientious care of the property of her patient and of the institution where she is employed. Any property which is stolen or unjustly damaged must be replaced or paid for by the guilty party.

Unjust damage is that damage which is the result of some fault on the part of the nurse, such as malice, carelessness, neglect. Unjust damage does not include accidents which may occur in the conscientious performance of duty. No restitution is due in such cases. In cases of doubt, the matter should be discussed with a priest.

A Day's Work for a Day's Pay

The nurse as a professional person deserves proper compensation for the services she renders. However, she can never afford to forget the fact that an honest day's pay deserves an honest day's work. Serious negligence in providing the services paid for would be a serious sin; slight negligence, a slight sin. Such negligence, being a form of theft, gives rise to the obligation of restitution. The nurse's constant attitude, "A day's work for a day's pay," will preclude any worries of conscience in later life.

Professional Secrecy

Secrets

While caring for the sick, the nurse may come into the possession of knowledge about the patient or the patient's family. If the facts are not commonly known, the nurse is bound to keep secret the information obtained in her professional capacity. This requirement is not only moral but also legal, the nurse's knowledge being classified legally as "privileged."

This obligation pertains to all secrets whether written or verbal, whether resulting from physical examination or observation. Particular care might well be taken in regard to secrets disclosed through the use of narcotherapy or "truth serum" or while the patient is under hypnosis.

Revelation of Secrets

The nurse may reveal a professional secret to prevent grave harm to herself. She must reveal it to prevent grave harm to (1) the patient, (2) an innocent third party, or (3) the community.

An example of harm coming to society as a whole would be the case of a very contagious disease. In such a case there would be an obligation to take whatever steps might be legally required in order to protect other people from the disease.

Another instance of the good of society in general being involved would be the classic example of the dangerous criminal who comes to seek treatment for stab or gunshot wounds. Civil law often requires that such cases be reported to the civil authorities. The moral basis justifying the revelation of a professional secret in the case of such criminals is not the fact that the criminal is fleeing justice, but rather that he constitutes a present threat to society and as such must be turned over to the police.

Truthfulness

"You shall be as Gods" (Gen. 3:5).

This was the first lie, uttered by the prince of darkness to Eve in the garden of paradise. Ever since that fateful day, lies and liars have been the target of severe censure. Ecclesiasticus tells us bluntly that "a lie is a foul blot in a man" (Ecclus. 20:26). And again, "A thief is better than a man that is always lying" (Ecclus. 20:27). The Book of Proverbs contains a familiar quotation: "Lying lips are an abomination to the Lord" (Prov. 12:22). Christ Himself, in one of His vigorous condemnations of the hypocritical Pharisees, referred to the devil as a liar and the father of lies (John 8:44). Even among worldly men, the epithet "Liar!" has long been taken as one of the worst of insults. Indeed, we search the pages of history almost in vain for a record of those who have advocated lying as a general practice. The Communists stand out as an exception: their teaching that one should lie to further the aims of the party merely adds another diabolical doctrine to a list already long and already condemned by right-thinking men.

The universal condemnation of lies and liars in itself seems to indicate that lying is contrary to the natural law. It is impossible to imagine the confusion that would result if we had no obligation to speak the truth. Most philosophers as well as theologians hold that lying is intrinsically immoral.

Lies and Falsehoods

The usual definition of a lie is this: *A lie is a communication contrary to what is in one's mind.* The traditional argument given as a proof of the intrinsic immorality of lying may be briefly stated as follows: Speech is given to man as a means of expressing what is in his mind. To use that faculty to deceive others, by speaking contrary to one's mind, is a reversal of God's plan and therefore sinful. (It is of course understood that, when we use the term "speech" in this context, we are including any word or act used to communicate thought.)

The classical argument to prove the intrinsic immorality of lying has been called the "perverted-faculty argument" and has been paralleled with the usual argument against contraception. It is summed up succinctly in the phrase "lies are wrong because they pervert the gift of speech." Saint Thomas says that since words are the natural expression of thoughts, it is unnatural and unbecoming that anyone should express what is not in his mind.[1]

However, some theologians hold a different view. They hold that in certain unusual circumstances it is justifiable to tell a falsehood.

Consider the case of a spy who is acting out of patriotism, which is a virtue—and yet his whole life at times is a deception. He falsifies his identity, his work, and his daily endeavors. Yet, in-

[1] Saint Thomas, *Summa*, 2.2, q. 110, a.3, c.

stinctively we judge what he is doing as good; he may be helping to protect his country in a just war, and yet he is doing this by deception. Consider a detective who, in order to apprehend a dangerous criminal, poses as and identifies himself as a plumber. Must we say that he is guilty of lying and therefore guilty of sin? Are we to hold that no one has a moral right to be a detective, as that profession is normally accepted and practiced? Are we to hold that practically all detectives are to be considered liars? One who holds that a lie is any speaking contrary to one's mind, and always by its nature evil, is hard put to give a convincing answer to questions such as these. Just as we instinctively hold a liar in contempt, so also we instinctively respect the detective who cleverly traps a criminal, or the nurse who withholds medical secrets from a prying hospital visitor.

Because of the difficulties involved in maintaining that every "speaking contrary to the mind" is a sin, there is another school of thought on this subject. These theologians give a different definition of a lie, making a distinction between a lie and a falsehood: *A lie is an untruth told to one who has a right to the truth; a falsehood is an untruth told to one seeking knowledge to which he has no right.* Some hint of this distinction seems to be found in the popular usage of the words. To accuse a man of telling a lie is much stronger than to declare that he told a falsehood.

Those who hold that falsehoods may sometimes be told point out that the "speaking contrary to the mind" definition omits consideration of a very important factor: The right of the listener to know the facts. The right of a person to knowledge from another is not absolute (as is his right to life) but relative (like his right to property) and must be judged in relationship to the rights of others. The hearer has a right to be treated always with justice and charity, but neither of these virtues requires that he be told the truth in all circumstances. There may be times when the right or duty of the speaker to withhold the truth, even by a false statement, is superior to the right of the listener to be given the truth. The welfare of society and the rights of men forbid false statements in the vast majority of cases, but—hold some theologians—there are exceptions.

Protection of professional secrets by doctors and nurses would on rare occasions constitute such exceptions.

The opinion that certain falsehoods are licit is sometimes considered a modern opinion, but it was held by various writers all the way back to Origen and Cassian, and back beyond them to Plato and the Stoics. It undoubtedly arises in large measure from a desire to defend one's right to protect secrets when circumstances exist that make mental reservations useless or at least too much of a gamble.

Therefore there are two schools of thought on the matter of truthfulness. One holds that a person may never speak contrary to his mind under any circumstances. The other holds that for a *grave reason* and in *exceptional circumstances*, a falsehood may be told without sin to a person who is seeking information *to which he has no right*. Where the authorities disagree, you are free to decide which school of thought you will follow.[2]

Categories of Lies

Theologians are in agreement that a lie will not constitute a mortal sin in itself. The act of lying can exceed venial sin at times when some other virtue is offended. Lies are divided into three categories: jocose, officious, and malicious.

Jocose lies are lies told for the sake of enjoyment. If they are really lies, they are sins. If, however, a person makes a joking remark which can be known as such by his demeanor or some other external circumstance, then no sin is committed because no lie has been told. Jocose lies are usually venial sins but could be mortal by reason of grave harm caused.

An *officious lie* may be described by the term "lie of convenience." Under the heading of officious lies come not only excuses but also lies originating in a spirit of boastfulness and pride. It is difficult to imagine an officious lie constituting grave matter.

[2] Cf. Rev. Julius A. Dorszynski, *Catholic Teaching about the Morality of Falsehood*, Washington, D.C.: The Catholic University of America Press, 1948.

A *malicious lie* is a lie that causes harm to another. It is a common practice to consider all malicious lies as grave. Although it seems probable that many malicious lies are in fact grave, nevertheless they are not grave as lies but only when they cause grave harm.

Ordinary folk persist in adding a fourth class of lies, the so-called "white lies." The term "white lie" is a popular term for an officious lie, a lie of excuse or convenience.

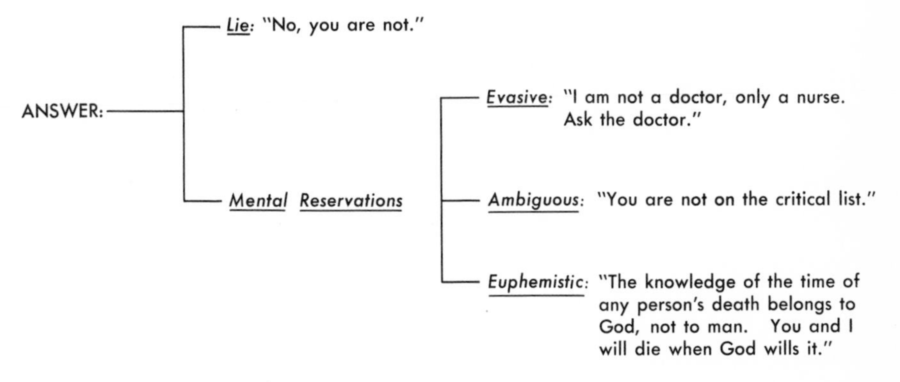

Figure 13. Mental reservations.

Theologically, the white lie is easily disposed of. If we follow the common opinion that every lie is a sin, then a white lie is a sin. And even if we hold that a person may make a false statement for a grave reason to one unjustly seeking information, we would still classify a white lie as a sin because hurt feelings or mere convenience do not constitute a grave reason for telling a falsehood.

Mental Reservations

A mental reservation is an evasive, ambiguous, or euphemistic statement to one who has no right to the truth. Mental reservations are morally permissible where there exists a right to conceal the facts and the person addressed has no right to the truth. The way this would work out in practice is illustrated by Figure 13.

In spite of the fact that circumstances may sometimes require the use of mental reservations in the medical profession, let it be remembered that they must not be used indiscriminately. They are only morally permissible when there exists an adequate reason to conceal the facts and the person addressed has no right to the truth but is attempting unjustly to obtain it. When used without sufficient reason, or in violation of a person's right to know the facts, mental reservations become a moral evil.

Conclusions

In summary, the following points might be given relative to the norms which may be utilized prudently in judging one's actions:

A lie is an untruth told to one to whom we have no right to tell a falsehood. Ordinarily speaking a person must be presumed to have a right to the truth.

A falsehood is an untruth told to one seeking information to which he has no right. This may be utilized in very restricted circumstances and for a grave reason.

A mental reservation is an evasive, ambiguous, or euphemistic statement to one who has no right to the truth. In this case, what is said is true, at least in some sense. In practice, when a person has no right to the truth, it is ordinarily by means of mental reservation, not a falsehood, that the situation can best be handled morally.

Disclosure of Medical Information

Warning the Patient in Danger of Death

The relatives have the first obligation of informing a patient as to the nature and seriousness of his illness. If they fail to fulfill this obligation, it then devolves upon the doctor. Finally, in the failure of both the relatives and the doctor, it becomes the duty of the nurse to tell the patient.

The purpose for which a man is placed in the world is to save his soul. The salvation of his soul depends on its condition at the moment of his death. It has been well said that the most important moment of a man's life is the moment of his death. If a person knows that he is in danger of death, he can prepare himself. If he does not realize that he is in danger, he may die unprepared and lose his soul.

It follows, then, that it is of the utmost importance that a patient in proximate danger of death be informed of his situation. The pagan practice of easing a person out of this world in ignorance is a terrible disservice to the patient concerned. The nurse should do whatever she can to eradicate this un-Christian custom.

Telling the Patient the Nature of His Illness

Every man is endowed by God with certain rights, and among these is the right to be told the nature of his illness. However, by force of some particular circumstance he may lose the right. Every man, as a man, has the right. It is only by reason of some accidental situation that he might cease to have the right. In other words, as the philosophers would say, *per se* the patient has the right, but *per accidens* he may not.

When should this right be denied? When should a patient not be told the nature of his illness? He should not be told if he would use the information against himself. If a man owns a revolver, he has a right to it; but if he intends to use it to commit suicide, then, because of that circumstance, he may be deprived of the possession of the revolver while the danger is present. The same applies with regard to a particular disease. The patient has the right to know; but in certain circumstances the facts may be withheld from him.

The classic example, of course, is cancer. To hold that every single cancer patient will suffer a mental breakdown when given his diagnosis is to hold a principle which is contrary to fact. There are many noble Christian souls who would use such information to great spiritual advantage. Moreover, the practice of wholesale deception by doctors is gravely injurious to the confidence which the public should have in the medical profession. Let each case be judged on its own merits, as justice demands.

Right of the Family and the Priest to Medical Information

Although we may grant that accidental circumstances may sometimes make it imprudent to inform the patient of medical facts, we cannot hold any such principle with regard to his family. The doctor is obliged to inform a responsible and representative relative of the diagnosis and prognosis. The custom of deceiving the family is to be condemned.

The priest will need to have a clear medical picture in order to fulfill the commands of Our Lord in regard to the various ministrations required. The nurse should realize that her hospital chaplain is part of the hospital family and promptly give him such information as he requires. This does not involve a violation of professional secrecy.

The Patient as an Individual

Refusal of Medical Care

Since the patient is obliged under sin to use the ordinary means of preserving his life and health, the nurse is bound in charity to put such means at his disposal. If he refuses to use them, she should do whatever is morally possible to make him use them. In such a situation, the nurse uses force in an attempt to prevent sin. The amount of force would be dictated by prudence and would vary in proportion to the grave consequences of the refusal. In the average case of a routine medication, a mere admonition would suffice; in the case of grave threat to life, such as attempted suicide, physical force might be necessary. However, no one should be forced to use any means which is extraordinary.

Beware of Routine

In the course of long months and years dealing with various cases, matters sometimes become strictly routine. At no time, however, can the nurse afford to forget that the patient is a person and treat him merely as a case number.

In this regard, a particular difficulty exists in the operating room, where the patient at times is not aware of the nurse's attitude. Nevertheless, the very life of the patient often depends on a flawless technique, and such a technique cannot long be maintained if the nurse loses her realization that she is dealing with human beings. Those who work among mental patients may at times find it especially difficult to avoid forgetting these facts.

It is possible that the nurse could become so hardened that she would lose her awareness of the patient's feelings in the matter of modesty. The nurse must never forget that an "ordinary" medical procedure may be a shocking and embarrassing experience to the patient. She should frequently recall the fact that the human body is the temple of the Holy Spirit.

On the other hand, it could happen that a nurse would experience temptation in the performance of her duty. In such a situation, it is sufficient to keep in mind that, although an occasion of sin may be present, the performance of duty makes it a necessary occasion and that, when prudent steps to avoid sin have been taken, there is no cause for concern.

The individuals with whom the nurse deals are not merely animals. They are creatures endowed with inalienable rights, having souls which were redeemed at the cost of the Precious Blood of Jesus Christ.

Topics for Discussion

Items may be true, partly true, erroneous, or unsolvable. First judge, then discuss.

1. It is always preferable to keep a cancer patient unaware of his diag-

nosis because in most cases great anxiety follows upon such information.

2. There is an old saying "finder's keeper's." Does this ever apply in your work?
3. List some situations in which a mental reservation could be used in good conscience.

Cases for Solution

1. A visitor asks the nurse if his brother who is a patient has been to confession, since he is concerned about his spiritual welfare. The nurse knows that the priest visited the patient but wonders whether this should be kept under professional secrecy.
2. A nurse receives an invitation to a wedding. She knows professionally that the bride has had a hysterectomy and discovers that the groom is unaware of his future wife's sterility. Has she a right to reveal this? Has she an obligation to reveal this?
3. A very prominent person is admitted to the hospital and given a fictitious name to protect his identity. In speaking of this patient how would you handle the situation without violating the Eighth Commandment?

References for Further Study

Healy, E. F. *Moral Guidance*, Chicago: Loyola University Press, 1960.

McFadden, C. J. *Medical Ethics*, 5th ed., Philadelphia: F. A. Davis Company, 1961.

O'Donnell, T. J. *Morals in Medicine*, Westminster, Md.: The Newman Press, 1956.

Regan, R. *Professional Secrecy in the Light of Moral Principles*, Washington, D.C.: Augustinian College, 1943.

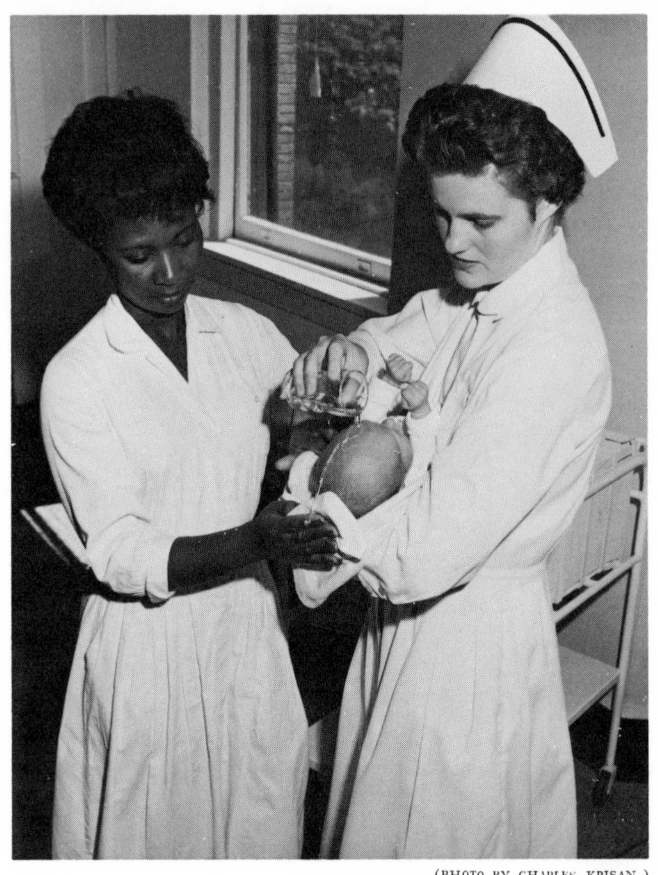
(PHOTO BY CHARLES KRISAN.)

St. Mary's Hospital, Orange, New Jersey.

CHAPTER II

Spiritual Care of the Patient

Spiritual care of the non-Catholic patient · Spiritual care of the Catholic patient · Baptism · Confession · Communion · Spiritual care of the seriously ill · The nurse's task includes the spiritual

Spiritual Care of the Non-Catholic Patient

Charity Toward All

The nurse should be interested in the salvation of all her patients, non-Catholic as well as Catholic. A nurse who confines her offer of spiritual aid to Catholics alone would hardly be worthy of praise for such an attitude.[1]

However, charity toward all must not involve a watering down of principles. The eternal truths handed down to the Church of Jesus Christ must never be compromised.

The nurse can well apply in her relation with the non-Catholic patients the axiom "Firm in principle, kindly in manner."

Calling the Minister or Rabbi

It is the teaching of the Catholic Church that ministers of all non-Catholic religions (be they in good faith or not) are in spiritual

[1] Cf. Section IV in *Dimensions of Professional Nursing* by Cordelia W. Kelly, New York: The Macmillan Company, 1962.

error. Since it is her duty to practice only the true religion, the Catholic nurse must take care to avoid either taking active part in the services of any non-Catholic sect or appearing by her actions or words to give approval to such a sect.

If a non-Catholic patient requests that a minister or rabbi be called, the Catholic nurse, in putting through the call, should take care not to cooperate in their religion by requesting religious rites. A simple request like "Mr. Jones is sick; will you come and see him?" will fulfill the patient's request without compromising principles.

Assisting the Minister or Rabbi

The Catholic nurse may courteously provide for the needs of the minister or rabbi by getting him a chair, putting the screen around the bed, or the like. It would not be allowed, however, for her to take an active part in the ministrations, since this would constitute formal cooperation in a false religion.

A berith or ritualistic circumcision offers no occasion of participation to a Catholic nurse. Jewish law makes her inadmissible to participation in the ceremony by reason of the fact that she is a non-Jew and a woman.

Baptism of the Children of Non-Catholics

If the non-Catholic patient is an infant or has not yet reached the use of reason and is in extreme danger of death, he should be baptized. This procedure is necessary because baptism is absolutely required for salvation. Pope Pius XII says:

> The state of grace at the moment of death is absolutely necessary for salvation. Without it, it is not possible to attain supernatural happiness, the beatific vision of God. An act of love can suffice for an adult to obtain sanctifying grace and supply for the absence of baptism; for the unborn child or for the newlyborn, this way is not open.[2]

[2] Address to Catholic midwives, October 29, 1951.

Since an infant does not possess the use of reason, it is impossible that he would have baptism of desire. Baptism of water is therefore the only means of saving his soul. However, it should not be carried out unless the infant is practically sure to die.

We cannot safely presume baptism in the case of non-Catholics because Protestant sects in many cases either do not baptize at all, or defer baptism for several years, or baptize invalidly.

Any objection to baptism on the part of the parents would be unreasonable, since this is the one means of getting their child into heaven. The nurse should do her utmost to administer this most important sacrament.

Non-Catholic Adults in Danger of Death

In the case of a non-Catholic adult who is in danger of death, the patient may be in good faith concerning his own religious affiliations, or he may suspect the truth of the claims of the Catholic Church.

1. If the patient gives indication of a desire to learn more of the Catholic Church or shows that he feels an urge of conscience to seek further the will of God, it is possible that God is offering him the grace to embrace the true Faith. In such an eventuality, the priest should be notified. He will handle the situation with tact and skill and take whatever steps are indicated. The nurse should, if possible, delay administration of narcotics until the priest arrives.

2. If the patient is in good faith (that is, he is following his conscience insofar as God has enlightened him), it is a great spiritual service to assist him to excite in his soul the dispositions which are required for salvation. These dispositions are: belief in God, who rewards the good and punishes the wicked; belief in the Trinity; belief in the Son of God as the Redeemer; hope of salvation; sorrow for sin; purpose of amendment; and love of God.

There has been prepared a prayer which embraces all of these acts and dispositions. The use of this prayer with dying non-Catholics is a great act of charity and is most highly recommended. The text of the prayer follows:

My Daily Prayer[3]

I believe in one God. I believe that God rewards the good, and punishes the wicked.

I believe that in God there are three Divine Persons—God the Father, God the Son, and God the Holy Spirit.

I believe that God the Son became Man, without ceasing to be God. I believe that He is my Lord and my Saviour, the Redeemer of the human race, that He died on the Cross for the salvation of all men, that He died also for me.

I believe, on God's authority, everything that He has taught and revealed.

O my God, give me strong faith. O my God, help me to believe with lively faith.

O my God, Who art all-good and all-merciful, I sincerely hope to be saved. Help me to do all that is necessary for my salvation.

I have committed many sins in my life, but now I turn away from them, and hate them. I am sorry, truly sorry for all of them, because I have offended Thee, my God, Who art all-good, all-perfect, all-holy, all-merciful and kind, and Who died on the Cross for me.

I love Thee, O my God, with all my heart. Please forgive me for having offended Thee.

I promise, O God, that with Thy help I will never offend Thee again. My God, have mercy on me.

It is recommended that a nurse have a supply of these cards on hand at all times.

Spiritual Care of the Catholic Patient

Obligation to Receive Sacraments

Any Catholic patient might well use his time in the hospital

[3] The prayer is available in printed form in many languages and may be obtained by writing to the Apostolate to Aid the Dying, 60 Compton Road, Cincinnati 15, Ohio.

to better his soul as well as his body. This can best be accomplished by reception of the sacraments. Therefore confession and Holy Communion are to be recommended in any case. If surgery is anticipated, it would seem lax for the patient to forego confession and Holy Communion. When a patient is in danger of death, he is obliged to receive the sacraments under pain of mortal sin.

When a Catholic patient is admitted to a hospital, the nurse should do him the spiritual favor of informing him that a priest is available to care for his spiritual needs. If the patient is in danger of death, notification of the priest is an obligation.

Danger of Death

"Danger of death" as regards the administration of the sacraments differs occasionally from "danger of death" in the hospital sense of the term. Hospital "danger lists" or "critical lists" are very often arbitrary, whereas the "danger of death" for the administration of the sacraments acts as a clear-cut guide. "Danger of death" is any condition resulting from sickness, accident, or old age which constitutes even a remote threat to the life of the patient.

The Second Council of the Vatican, in its Constitution on the Sacred Liturgy, saw fit to stress this point:

> Extreme Unction, which may also and more fittingly be called "the anointing of the sick," is not a sacrament only for those who are at the point of death. As soon as one of the faithful begins to be in danger of death from sickness or old age, the appropriate time for him to receive this sacrament has definitely arrived.

When to Call the Priest

If the danger of death is very remote, such as in the case of an early cancer, casual reference to the situation when the priest is making his rounds will suffice. In more acute cases it is necessary to notify the priest immediately.

Prompt spiritual attention should be given in the case of cerebrovascular accident, coma, pulmonary edema, peritonitis, severe

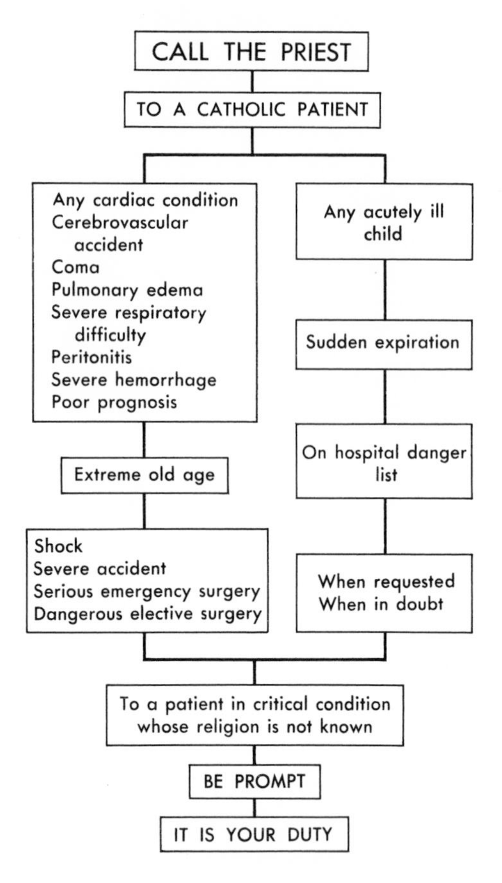

Figure 14. When to call the priest to a Catholic patient.

hemorrhage, any cardiac condition, shock, severe accidents, all patients about to undergo serious surgical operations, patients with poor prognosis, and those in danger of death from old age.

The priest should be notified when a child is acutely ill. Although it is true that a baptized child before the use of reason is not a subject for extreme unction, the priest would want to investigate the possibility of the use of reason occurring at an unusually early age. It is also possible that the child has not been baptized. This would hold true occasionally in the case of older children whose parents have been neglectful. It is also possible that a blessing would be the means of restoring the child to health.

The priest should be summoned to mental cases in danger of death unless it is certain that they have never possessed the use of reason. Even in this event the priest should ordinarily be informed since there might be question of the administration of baptism or confirmation.

The priest should be called promptly in the case of sudden expirations, because it is possible that the soul is still present and would receive the benefits of the last rites. Extreme unction may be administered conditionally up to several hours after sudden death, but quick action is important because the chances of success diminish as time goes on. In the case of death, sudden or not, where last rites have not been given, call the priest immediately and state the facts.

The priest should be called to any Catholic officially listed by the hospital as in "dangerous" or "critical" condition. Likewise, he should be called to any patient in critical condition whose religion is not known.

A good motto to follow is "When in doubt, call."

The request of a patient or his relatives to see a priest should be complied with promptly.

If it is at all possible, delay administration of narcotics until the priest has arrived. To deprive the patient of his senses before calling the priest may deprive him of the opportunity to express sorrow for sin and make his confession.

Remember: It is a mortal sin to deliberately neglect necessary spiritual care of a patient in danger of death!

Will the Priest Frighten the Patient?

When a patient is dangerously ill, the nurse proceeds to do what is best for his physical condition. She does not ask him if he would like to see the doctor; she calls the doctor. Perhaps he dislikes doctors; perhaps he is afraid of doctors; but she calls the doctor anyway. She does what is best for the patient. She knows that any objection on his part is unreasonable.

The patient's spiritual care should be handled in the same way. When a Catholic patient is dangerously ill, the nurse proceeds to do what is best for him. She does not ask him if he would like to see the priest; she calls the priest. Perhaps he dislikes priests; perhaps he is afraid of priests; but she calls the priest anyway. She does what is best for the patient. She knows that any objection on his part is unreasonable.

The doctor may find it necessary to cause the patient some pain in order to save his life; the priest may find it necessary to cause him some pain to save his soul. Surely no patient likes pain, but at the same time he has no reasonable objection to the saving of his life or the saving of his soul.

What the doctor does, what the priest does, is their concern. You have done your duty in notifying them.

The fear that a patient will be apprehensive is not a reason for refusing to call the priest. Would you refuse to warn a blind man who is walking on the edge of a precipice? If fear or apprehension were a reason, the priest would seldom be called, and so we would disobey the command of Christ.

Salvation of a Soul Is Everybody's Business

A person's soul is the business of God, the priest (who is intermediary between God and man), and the person himself. Less proximately, it is also the business of others, who, by reason of an opportunity to help him in the salvation of his soul, are so bound in charity.

The patient who registers as a Catholic obviously wishes to be treated as a Catholic.

If a doctor attempts to deprive the patient of his spiritual rights by ordering you not to call the priest, a grave moral obligation requires you to call anyway. And in such a case, tell the priest so that he can take proper steps to protect other Catholics from being harmed.

A priest's life is dedicated to saving souls. If your patients need him, please call. No hour of the day or night will be out of place. The salvation of souls is more important than any earthly good.

The Priest, the Only Divinely Appointed Physician of Souls

Although everyone should assist in the salvation of souls, nevertheless the personal relationship of a soul to God is the concern only of those whom God has appointed. Priests are charged by divine commission with the care of souls and the custody of the sacraments. It is not within the province of hospital authorities, nuns, doctors, or nurses to question the policies and procedures of the chaplain regarding his priestly ministrations, or to encroach upon his divinely appointed field of work. The attitude of all toward the administration of the sacraments and the care of souls must be one of respectful cooperation and obedience. No garb or uniform, no degree or administrative position, no amount of good intentions invests a person with the prerogatives of the priesthood.

A soul is the most private of private property, and we may enter only when invited or when authorized by Almighty God. Nursing is for nurses; religious life for religious; but the care of souls and the custody of the sacraments is the responsibility of priests of Jesus Christ.

Baptism

Requisites for Baptism

The priest is the ordinary minister of baptism. However, in case of emergency anyone else can and should baptize. It is preferable, but not essential, that a Catholic perform the ceremony.

For a valid baptism, the following three requisites must be considered:

1. The *matter* of baptism is plain natural water. Holy water is not necessary. It is to be noted that saline solution is not plain natural water.

2. The *form* consists of the words: "I baptize you in the name of the Father and of the Son and of the Holy Spirit."[4] The words should be spoken audibly so that at least the one baptizing can hear them. The giving of a name is not essential.

3. The person baptizing must have the *intention* of doing what Christ or the Catholic Church wishes. A nurse who seriously intends to confer baptism need not trouble herself about the proper intention, because her very action is a proof and guarantee of that intention.

How to Baptize

A nurse who is baptizing should pour ordinary water on the forehead (not on the hair) of the person to be baptized and say while pouring the water: "I baptize you in the name of the Father and of the Son and of the Holy Spirit."

Cautions Regarding the Administration of Baptism

Since the sacrament of baptism is essential for eternal salvation, several factors should be considered to assure validity in its administration.

1. The pouring of the water and saying of the words should be simultaneous.

2. The same person must pour the water and say the words.

3. The water must flow on the skin. In the case of newborns, remove the vernix caseosa.

4. The water should flow on the head. If circumstances make

[4] Some books give the form, "I baptize *thee* in the Name of the Father, and of the Son, and of the Holy *Ghost*."

EMERGENCY BAPTISM	
What to use:	Ordinary water.
Intention:	To do what the Roman Catholic Church wishes.
What to do:	While you are pouring the water on the forehead (not the hair) of the person to be baptized, speak the required words audibly.
What to say:	"I baptize you in the name of the Father and of the Son and of the Holy Spirit."

Figure 15. Instructions for emergency baptism.

this impossible (such as difficult delivery), the water should be poured on the presenting part nearest the head. Since the validity of such a baptism is doubtful, conditional baptism in the normal way should follow if possible.

5. If it is not possible to pour water on the head of the fetus, it should be immersed in a basin of water while the words of baptism are spoken. Note: Sterile water is valid matter for baptism;

saline is doubtful. We are never allowed to choose doubtful matter where the eternal salvation of a soul is at stake. Therefore do not use saline to baptize. Sterile water may be used.

6. Every word of the form should be said distinctly.

7. Be careful not to have a conditional intention depending on a future event; for example, do not have the intention of baptizing only on condition that the child will die. The intention should simply be to baptize this individual if he is capable here and now of being baptized.

Conditional Baptism

When it is doubtful that a person is capable of receiving baptism, conditional baptism is administered. Such might be the case when there is doubt concerning the presence of life, or doubt of a previous baptism. In any case of conditional baptism, the following form may be used: "If you are capable of receiving baptism, I baptize you in the name of the Father and of the Son and of the Holy Spirit." If the conditional words are forgotten or omitted for some reason, the usual words of baptism are sufficient for validity. A baptism that is not conditional is referred to as "absolute."

Baptism of Infants

When an infant is in danger of death, a priest should be called to administer baptism. If there is not sufficient time, the nurse should perform the baptism.

Baptism of Ectopics

Ectopic pregnancy includes any displaced implantation. The most frequent site is the fallopian tube. Sometimes the tube ruptures spontaneously, and sometimes an unruptured tube is excised as a pathologic organ. Unfortunately, it is usually impossible to administer baptism in either case, because of the difficulty of identifying the embryo, which is very tiny. If an embryo is identified, or even probably identified, and if it might be alive, it should be baptized.

Baptism of Monstrosities

Every living product of human conception regardless of its deformity should be baptized.

Baptism of Stillborns

Unless the newborn is certainly dead, baptism should be administered. The only certain sign of death is putrefaction. Even after declared death, there may still be a possibility of life. If there is any hope of life at all, baptism should be administered conditionally.

Intrauterine Baptism

If it seems probable that a fetus will be dead before delivery and a Caesarian section is not indicated, intrauterine baptism should be attempted unless this procedure would endanger the life of the mother. If the fetus is viable, the membranes should first be ruptured and the amniotic fluid drained off. Sterile water should be used. Any irrigating instrument such as a syringe and cannula may be used. The tube end of the instrument is passed through the os and, while the water is directed against the fetus, the words of baptism are pronounced. This baptism should be administered conditionally and, if possible, repeated conditionally under more favorable circumstances.

The membranes should not be ruptured in the case of a nonviable fetus, since this would constitute a direct attack on the life of the fetus. In this situation, baptism is impossible. However, if the membranes should rupture spontaneously, intrauterine baptism should be attempted.

Baptism When a Mother Has Died

"Immediately after the death of a pregnant mother, a Caesarian section should be performed so that the fetus may be baptized" (Canon 746). Hospital administrators should strive to make the fulfillment of this Church law possible by establishing admitting procedures that meet the requirements of common law or any pertinent civil enactment.

Baptism in Case of Abortion

In any case of abortion—spontaneous, criminal, or therapeutic—an attempt should be made to baptize the fetus. In most cases, baptism is performed in the usual way. In the early weeks of pregnancy when the fetus would not be identified easily, the product of conception should be immersed in water while the words of baptism are pronounced. Obviously the baptism of membranes is useless, and the nurse's efforts in each case should be directed toward the baptism of the fetus proper.

Sponsors in Baptism

When infant or adult baptism is administered in case of emergency, a sponsor should be used if possible. In this way an official witness to this important ceremony is provided. The sponsor should be a Catholic and should touch the subject during the baptism. However, the presence of a sponsor is not of sufficient importance to occasion a dangerous delay in the administration of emergency baptism.

Recording and Reporting the Baptism

Whenever the sacrament of baptism is administered, the fact should be recorded immediately in the customary place. Nurses who are in a position to make suggestions or set a policy regarding the recording of baptism or other sacraments should take steps to

REPORT OF EMERGENCY BAPTISM

To Be Sent Immediately to Catholic Chaplain

Name of person baptized (print) ________________

Check: ☐ Living ☐ Probably living ☐ An aborted fetus ☐ Apparently dead but not macerated

Date of birth __________ Date of baptism __________

Father's first name (print) ________________

Mother's first name (print) ________________

Mother's maiden name (print) ________________

Witness to baptism, if any (print) ________________

Remarks ________________________________

____

This is to certify that I, having the intention of doing what the Roman Catholic Church wishes, administered baptism to the above-described person by pouring ordinary water upon the forehead and saying audibly at the same time, "I baptize you in the name of the Father and of the Son and of the Holy Spirit."

____
Signature

Figure 16. Suggested form for reporting emergency baptism.

see that clear, permanent, and easily accessible records are kept. One very helpful method is to record baptism or last rites on the patient's chart.

Any baptism of an infant or an adult, besides being recorded in the hospital records, should be reported to the priest. Whenever possible, the following information should be obtained: the name of the person baptized, address, date of birth and baptism, father's name, mother's maiden name, and sponsor.

Confession

Honoring Request for Confession

When a patient requests that a priest be called to hear his confession, the request should be complied with promptly. The administration of any drug or anesthesia which would deprive the patient of the clear use of his reason should be deferred until the priest arrives. A patient in the operating room just prior to the operation may suddenly request a priest. Such a request might be inconsiderate, and surely it is inconvenient; nevertheless, it should be honored. Spiritually, it might be of great importance. Medically, it is indicative of apprehension which should be removed before proceeding. Requests of mental patients should be given honest consideration and complied with if the case so warrants.

Suggesting Confession

A tactful and kindly suggestion regarding confession is often appreciated by the patient, and no opportunity to do this kindness should be overlooked. However, the nurse must be on her guard lest she antagonize or offend any patient by seeming to be a zealot or to usurp the privileges of the chaplain.

Providing Privacy for Confession

The hospital offers many problems regarding privacy for confession. When it is impossible to secure privacy, absolution may be given upon a general expression of sorrow for sin and without a detailed confession. However, privacy should be provided if possible because the patient who is merely given absolution has an obligation of making a detailed statement of his mortal sins when he next goes to confession.

The nurse may find these suggestions helpful in her efforts to assist the priest:

1. Use a screen or curtains.

2. Shut the door.

3. If the patient is ambulatory, a little assistance to walk to a more private location might be in order.

4. If it seems feasible, politely ask other patients to leave the room for a few minutes.

5. If the family is present, request them to leave. Call them back after confession if other sacraments are to be administered.

6. Sometimes a radio or television set turned on—not off—will be helpful in providing privacy for confession. First ask the priest if he desires this. Turn it off when the priest proceeds to other rites.

7. If privacy cannot be obtained within the room, and the patient is nonambulatory and seems to desire full discussion with the priest, try to move the bed out of the room. This procedure may be medically indicated to remove apprehension based on spiritual difficulties.

8. No notation regarding confession should be kept in the medical records, nor should the priest be questioned on the matter. However, it would be proper to inquire of the patient whether he wishes to be placed on the Communion list.

Communion

Importance of the Blessed Sacrament

There are many important visitors to the hospital floors, but by far the most important is Jesus Christ. It is indeed Our Lord Himself who comes when the priest carries the Blessed Sacrament, bringing Holy Communion to the patients.

The honor and respect which the busy nurse shows to Our Lord in this great sacrament will be a measure of the love for Jesus which burns in her heart. She prepares for His coming with joy; she shows her loyalty by kneeling in His presence; she counts it the highest of honors to assist at the side of His priest. She kindly admonishes others to be quiet in His presence; her love for Him is a constant example, inspiring the respect of others, even those not of the Faith.

Communion to Those in Danger of Death ("Viaticum")

"In danger of death from whatever cause, the faithful are obliged to receive Holy Communion. . . . As long as the danger of death remains, it is allowed and it is fitting that they receive Holy Viaticum repeatedly on different days, in accordance with prudent advice of a confessor" (Canon 864). No fast is required in such cases.

Communion to Those Not in Danger of Death

The Church encourages frequent and even daily Communion. In order to show respect for the Blessed Sacrament, the Church imposes certain fasting regulations upon those not in danger of death.

The ordinary rules of Communion fast for Catholics in general require that the subject abstain for three hours from solid foods and alcoholic beverages, and for one hour from nonalcoholic liquids. Water does not break the fast.

The sick, even if not bedridden, may take nonalcoholic liquids and that which is really and truly medicine, either in liquid or solid form, before Holy Communion without any time limit.[5]

"The Eucharistic Communion!" exclaims Pope Pius XII. "The Divine King gives Himself to us! If only we truly knew and appreciated this gift of Infinite Love! . . . This Mystery of life, this divine medicine of immortality sustains the life of the soul, restores strength and renews it, neutralizes the germs of vice and makes all virtues germinate."[6]

[5] *Motu Proprio* of Pope Pius XII, March 19, 1957.

[6] Address of Pope Pius XII to the International Eucharistic Congress at Rio de Janeiro, July 24, 1955. Translated from the original Portuguese.

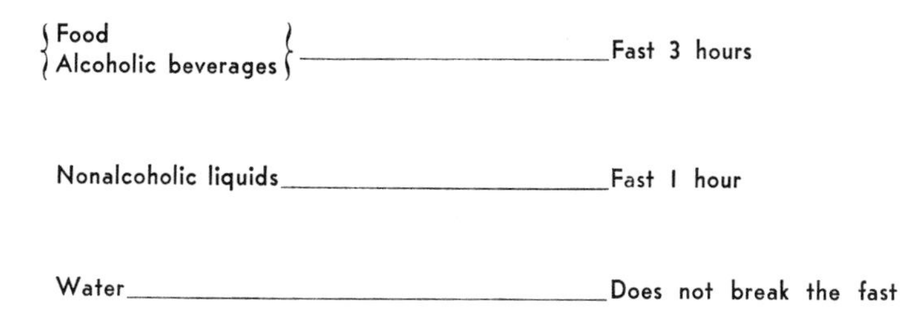

Figure 17A. Communion fast for Catholics in general.

Preparing for Communion

Before the priest arrives, elevate the patient slightly, unless this is contraindicated. Be sure that the patient is dressed modestly. Clear the table. Place it at the foot of the bed or at least in a position where it will not obstruct the priest. The table should be covered with a white cloth, linen if possible.

1. *Minimum requirements for Communion table:* Crucifix, two candles, glass of water, teaspoon, and holy water if available.

2. *Communion table in Catholic hospital:* Crucifix, two candles, glass of water, finger towel, teaspoon, ritual, open corporal, burse, holy water.

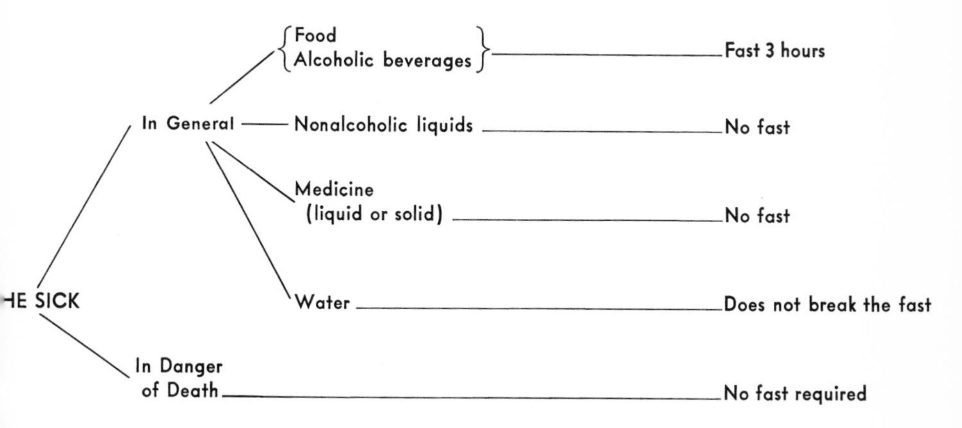

Figure 17B. Communion fast for the sick.

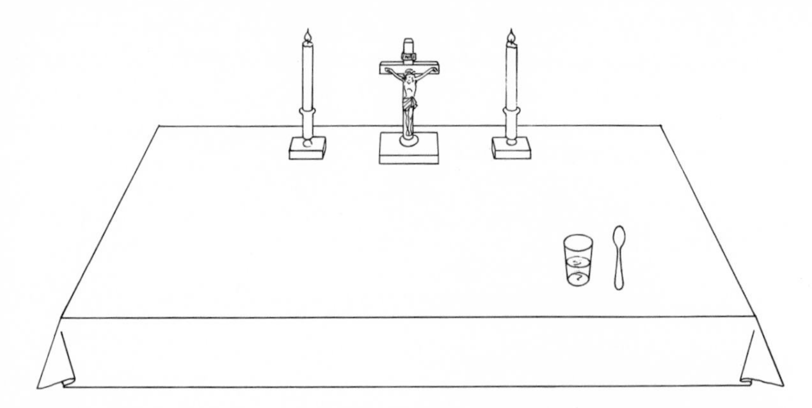

Figure 18A. Table for Communion—minimum requirements. Table should be covered with plain white cloth, linen if possible. Leave space front-center for Blessed Sacrament.

3. *When several are receiving:* Set up one Communion table in a convenient location, and place a glass of water at each bedside. If a particular patient may have difficulty in swallowing, place a teaspoon near his glass of water.

If the nurse informs the other patients in the room in a serious tone that the priest is coming with Communion, they will usually be silent and respectful.

Figure 18B. Table for Communion in a Catholic hospital.

In lighting a candle be careful to avoid the danger of fire by keeping flame at a safe distance from curtains or other inflammable material. If oxygen is being administered or stored in the room, the candles should *not* be lighted at all, and the priest should be warned of the danger of fire if he is not familiar with hospital work.

1. Prepare table.

2. Watch for arrival of priest.

3. Meet priest at door with lighted blessed candle.

4. Avoid unnecessary conversation.

5. Accompany priest to sickroom.

6. Provide privacy for confession.

7. Encourage all present to kneel in sickroom during Communion.

8. If priest is still carrying Blessed Sacrament, again accompany him to door with candle.

9. Extinguish candles promptly to avoid fire.

10. Leave patient undisturbed for thanksgiving prayers.

Figure 19. Suggestions for Communion of the sick at home.

The Nauseous Patient and Communion

Every effort should be made to forestall the danger of profanation of the Blessed Sacrament caused by vomiting after Holy Communion. Communion must not be given until vomiting has ceased and it seems certain that it will not recur. Each case must be judged individually, and the final decision must be left to the priest. Often the priest will ask the nurse's opinion. It is well to remember that, when there is danger that the Sacred Host may be expelled, the rule "In doubt—wait" should be applied.

If, perchance, the patient vomits after receiving Communion, these possibilities must be considered:

1. If half an hour has elapsed since the reception of Communion and the Host is not distinguishable, no steps need be taken.
2. If half an hour has not elapsed and the Host cannot be distinguished, the entire matter must be placed in a clean container or in a clean cloth and the priest notified immediately.
3. If the Host can be distinguished, It should be removed with a clean spoon from the other matter, placed in a clean container, and put under safekeeping until the priest arrives.

The danger of vomiting being absent, Communion may be given to a patient with gastric drainage as long as the drainage can be discontinued without harm to the patient for the length of time which the priest directs. In practice, Communion is not usually given to such cases.

Because of the stimulation of the vomiting reflex during the administration of some types of anesthesia, extreme caution should be exercised in preoperative Communion. As much time as possible should elapse between the reception of Communion and the administration of anesthesia.

Communion in Special Cases

Each individual case must be given separate consideration in the following categories:

SERIOUSLY ILL CHILDREN. The priest should be notified when any child, even as young as four or five years of age, is in danger of death or is expected to be a patient for a long period of time, in order that Holy Communion may be given if the case warrants it.

MENTAL CASES. Mental patients and the senile are allowed to receive Communion providing they are able to venerate the Sacrament as the Sacred Body of Our Lord and to receive It with reverent demeanor.

GASTRIC LAVAGE. Gastric lavage does not break the Communion

fast. Communion should be administered after the stomach has been washed, not before.

SUDDEN EXPIRATIONS. If a patient expires suddenly after receiving Communion, the nurse should determine whether the Host has been swallowed or not. If It has been swallowed, no further action is indicated. If not, the priest should be called immediately. If he is not available, the particles should be removed with a spoon, placed in a clean container, and put under safekeeping until he arrives.

Figure 20. Table for the sacrament of the sick.

Spiritual Care of the Seriously Ill

The sacrament of the sick (extreme unction, "last rites") has as its primary purpose the spiritual preparation of a Catholic in danger of death. In addition to this, the patient will also benefit physically if it is God's will.

Preparing the Table for the Sacrament of the Sick

Before the priest arrives for the administration of the sacrament of the sick, a table should be prepared as follows: white cloth, six small balls of cotton on a dish, crucifix, two candles, holy water, and ritual if available.

Assisting the Priest During Extreme Unction

The essential part of the sacrament of extreme unction is the anointing with holy oil of the "five senses" in this order: eyes, ears, nostrils, mouth, hands. The nurse may assist by turning the patient's head during the anointing of the ears and by holding the hands palms up. (The hands of a priest are anointed on the back instead of the palm.) The feet of the patient may be anointed at the discretion of the priest, and in such a case the nurse would uncover them after the anointing of the hands.

Whenever circumstances permit, the Catholic patient in danger of death will be given the following ministrations by the priest: (1) confession, (2) extreme unction, (3) Communion, and (4) last blessing. Cotton that has been used in the anointing should be burned.

The Nurse's Task Includes the Spiritual

The nurse's task involves countless physical ministrations relative to the sick and dying. However, many of her duties and opportunities revolve around the spiritual. This should never be allowed to take on the note of unimportance. Whether it be assisting the priest in administering the sacraments, administering the sacrament of baptism herself, giving spiritual consolation, or seizing an opportunity of encouraging proper sentiments, the nurse should ever keep in the back of her mind that she is dealing not merely with a human body but with a complete human personality which includes an immortal soul. As important as is her meticulous care in physical ministrations, the more far-reaching implications of her vocation revolve around the spiritual.

Topics for Discussion

Items may be true, partly true, erroneous, or unsolvable. First judge, then discuss.

1. Two Catholic nurses are discussing their obligations toward non-Catholic patients. One says that since she is convinced about the

truth and consolation of her Faith, everything possible should be done to convert a non-Catholic patient to Catholicism. The other nurse feels that this is not her place as a nurse.
2. A nurse is acquainted with a man who is a lapsed Catholic. He is admitted to the hospital as a non-Catholic and becomes seriously ill. What should she do?
3. Discuss the spiritual opportunities that a Catholic nurse has in a city hospital, in a Protestant hospital, in a Catholic hospital.

Cases for Solution

1. A mother expires in the labor room. Should intrauterine baptism be attempted?
2. An accident victim is brought into the emergency room in critical condition. One of the policemen tells the nurse that a priest was on the scene and that he feels certain that all necessary sacraments were administered. Should the nurse call the hospital chaplain or merely record this on the emergency form?
3. An infant in the premature nursery suddenly becomes critical. The nurse does not know what name the parents wish to confer on the child, and in addition no one is in the immediate area to act as a sponsor. What should she do?

References for Further Study

Connell, F. "Administration of Baptism to Unknown Dying Persons," *American Ecclesiastical Review*, May, 1945.
Curtis, W. W. *Call The Priest!* (pamphlet), New York: The Catholic Information Society, 1947.
Finney, Patrick, and O'Brien, Patrick. *Moral Problems in Hospital Practice*, St. Louis: B. Herder Book Co., 1956.
Godin, Edgar, and O'Hanley, J. P. E. *Hospital Ethics*, Bathhurst, New Brunswick, Canada: Hotel Dieu Hospital, 1957.
Gumpel, P. "Unbaptized Infants: May They Be Saved?", *Downside Review*, Bath, England: Downside Abbey, Autumn, 1954.
Jone, H., and Adelman, U. *Moral Theology*, Westminster, Md.: The Newman Press, 1953.
Kelly, G. "An Instruction on Baptism," *Hospital Progress*, February, 1949.
Woywod, S. "Consent of Parents Required for Baptism of Children," *Homiletic and Pastoral Review*, January, 1941.

IN YOUR LIFE, THERE ARE SO MANY SACRIFICES TO BE MADE, SO MANY DANGERS TO BE OVERCOME, THAT IT WOULD BE IMPOSSIBLE WITHOUT SUPERNATURAL HELP TO TRIUMPH CONSTANTLY OVER HUMAN WEAKNESS.

PIUS XII

Address to the nursing staff of Roman institutions, May 21, 1952.

PART IV

The Character of a Nurse

(RELIGIOUS NEWS SERVICE PHOTO.)

CHAPTER 12

Christianity's Answer to the Problem of Suffering

The medical profession and suffering · Love of God · The nurse who can help

A CERTAIN FEW PROBLEMS, old but ever new, have constantly been the source of discussion among men of every age, tantalizing Greek philosophers of old and moderns of the twentieth century alike. One of these is the problem of suffering.

Why was this child born deaf and blind? Why is it that often the good suffer and the evil go unpunished? Why does that aged patient who has outlived all who loved her linger on alone in her misery? Why are so many people mentally unbalanced?

A Nursing Problem

Rather frequently the nurse is called upon to help a patient resign himself to suffering, to prolonged confinement, or even to death. Occasionally she finds it necessary to console or admonish the family in the face of a great trial. In such situations, the most valuable help comes from the nurse who by her reading, her associations, and her prayers has learned Christianity's answer to the problem of suffering and has allowed that answer to penetrate deep into her soul. The nurse should lose no opportunity to read on this subject and to ponder over it. Especially should she treasure the remarks of those who are older and more experienced, and of those who are close to God, because a fuller comprehension of the problem of suffering is the reward of holiness and the fruit of long experience.

The hedonists before Christ recoiled from suffering, vainly offering the standard that pleasure is the chief good in life. But this was little help for humanity, which despite its efforts could not escape all suffering. That is why the Greek writers Sophocles and Euripides called life a misfortune. It is said that a pagan philosopher at his wit's end exclaimed: "The best thing in the world is not to be born; the next best, if we have to be born, is to die as quickly as possible." Through it all, the pagans realized the inadequacy of their answer.

Even many of the Jews, God's chosen people of the Old Law, although they saw suffering in a different light, did not have an explanation to fit the facts. Their idea was that any suffering, any affliction, was a punishment for sin. It was left for Christ to change this belief. On one occasion, a group of Jews were gathered about a blind man. There was an interesting test question they wished to put to Jesus, and so they drew His attention. "Rabbi, who has sinned, this man or his parents, to account for his being born blind?" And Jesus answered: "Neither this man has sinned, nor his parents. No. God simply wants to make use of him to reveal his ways" (John 9:2-3).

Christ's answer is a key to the suffering and affliction of this life: Such trials are sent or allowed by God but not necessarily as a punishment. Could it be that often they are a blessing in disguise? This is the answer that Christianity gives. The Christian idea of suffering is summed up by Saint Peter: "You have been called to suffer, because Christ on his part suffered for you, leaving you his example that you might follow in his footsteps" (I Pet. 2:21). If, then, we are to call ourselves Christians—followers of Christ—we may expect to find some trials in our life.

In times past the image of the cross was inseparable from the life of the Christian. It was the symbol that inspired hearts during the Crusades. There was a time when men in a dining hall would cross their knives and forks on the table after the meal, to remind themselves that the enjoyment of any pleasures in life should never lead them to forget the part of the cross of Christ in their lives. The apostles, gloriously spurred on by the figure of the Crucified, preached the crucifixion as the symbol of our salvation: "We preach Christ crucified."

The Medical Profession and Suffering

Today the cross finds no such intimate place in the life of many a modern Christian. It is rejected from public life, from schools and offices. One young woman doctor, after having finished her internship, was about to outfit an office and begin her own practice. One of the first pieces of equipment she put in her new office was a large crucifix. She remarked how the first several patients looked at the crucifix and then cast a glance at her as if they considered that she depended for cures on charms or symbols rather than her medical skill. The doctor remarked that many of her first patients did not see the intimate connection between her medical and scientific knowledge and the crucified Christ in her life.

This rejection of the practical place of the cross in our life is in part due to the spirit of secularism of our age, where Christ—and indeed religion in general—is separated from daily life.

The rejection of the cross is due in part also to the fact that sincere contemplation of the image of Christ hanging upon the cross can hardly help but awaken feelings of remorse and sorrow. Shame, sorrow, frank acknowledgment of guilt are not part of the pattern of "modern" man. Since these reactions spring naturally from thoughts of the Crucified, the Crucified is rejected. Christ is looked upon as a symbol of defeat, of failure. The very fact of a man's need for redemption, of his need for atonement for wrongs done, is foreign to the feelings of self-sufficiency and self-confidence of modern men and women.

Even for many a sincere Catholic, the deep sense of the significance of the lesson of Good Friday has somewhat waned. Perhaps it is because we have become so accustomed to looking at the crucifix. We see beautifully hand-carved crucifixes; we see delicate pearl bridal crucifixes. Every time we enter a Catholic Church, we see the crucifix in evidence. We look upon the crucifix every time we finger our rosary beads. We glance at it and then thoughtlessly turn away. Perhaps if we were given the grace of seeing things through the eyes of those who lived closer to Christ's own time we would realize more deeply what suffering and agony the cross implies, what love the cross represents. Those who lived closer to Christ's day had seen men nailed to a cross. They had seen a body stretched on a crossbar, red with blood, twisted with pain.

In Roman days, crucifixion was a death for hardened criminals and slaves. The Romans had a terror of this type of death, and no Roman citizen could be subjected to it.

Before being crucified, the victim was scourged. Then he was made to bear his cross through the busiest streets of the town to make the execution as public as possible. When the place of execution was reached, the prisoner was made to lie on the ground with arms outstretched and then his hands were nailed to the crosspiece. Then the victim was lifted up, the crosspiece nailed or tied to the vertical beam, and finally his feet nailed by the soldiers standing on the ground. There the victim awaited death.

Those who lived nearer to Christ's own time knew all this well, and as they looked at a crucifix and saw the figure of Christ, it meant so much more to them than it does to us.

If a nurse would take time to gaze for a while at a crucifix, not just glance and turn away, perhaps she could come to realize more deeply the agony and shame of Christ for love of us. Christ chose this path of suffering, the agony of this crucifixion, because of our sins and to prove unmistakably His love for us.

As she looks at that forehead pierced with thorns, that body red with blood, those hands with gaping wounds, that tongue swollen with thirst, her heart must begin to realize His love for every soul. "No one can give a greater proof of his love than by laying down his life for his friends" (John 15:13). When we realize Christ's tremendous sacrifices for us, then we begin to see we are falling short, that we are offering little proof of our love in return.

Have you ever stopped to consider in how many aspects of life we must give something before we can possess a desired object for ourselves? That is, of course, true when we purchase an article from the store. But it is true in a deeper and wider sense. The fact that we usually must give in order to get is true in the sphere of the immaterial as well as the material. It is true, for instance, in the case of knowledge. A person who has mastered astronomy or mathematics or medicine has given much of his energy and has sacrificed a great deal to gain the knowledge he now has. A teacher will tell you that he never profited so much from his subject when he merely studied it as when he began to teach it. It is when a teacher begins to give out the subject that he really gains a deep knowledge of it. A person is very happy himself if he can give something to make a loved one happy.

Love is like that. A person's love grows and deepens as he gives and sacrifices for the one he loves.

Love of God

This same principle is true in our relations with God. That is why suffering, sacrifice, penance, and generosity to God are necessary to obtain happiness and a shower of graces. That is why, if we love our life as Christ intended we should, there will be suffering involved; there will be joyful giving even before we begin to take on voluntary extra forms of penance. In the ordinary fulfilling of the duties of our state of life, there will be crosses; and the submissive, willing, and joyful acceptance of these will call down great blessings from the hand of God.

Before we proceed to take on extra forms of penance, we might well cultivate the proper attitude toward the crosses that God has already chosen to send us. The persevering fulfillment of the duties of our state of life is the expression of Christ's will for us, and to carry out this will is a most acceptable sacrifice before God. A nurse will have daily, indeed hourly, opportunities to live this truth.

The spirit of mere resignation to whatever trials God chooses to send us in our life can develop into courageous, even joyous endurance. We see the value of these things in Christ's plan. We see the fruit of patience, and love and courage grow; we see a means of atoning for sin and shortening purgatory; a means of becoming more Christlike. Through the crosses in our life, the fruit of love can blossom in our soul as it did for the sinful woman at Christ's feet: "Her sins, numerous as they are, are forgiven. You see, she has shown so much love!" (Luke 7:47).

When sickness strikes or moral trials come, it is then that the spirit of Christlike resignation is valuable.

Christ in the garden of Gethsemane begged to be spared from His cross: "Father, if it pleases you, spare me this cup!" But He hastened to add: "However, may your will, not mine, be done" (Luke 22:42).

When crosses and difficulties come, the reaction for the Christian is not "Why does God do this to me?" or "O Lord, not this," but rather "Your will be done."

If that spirit is deeply rooted in the life of a nurse, then by offering her trials, daily difficulties, and crosses to Christ, she will gain immeasurably more than she has given.

It is part of God's plan that suffering and trials, far from being a punishment, are a gift to those He loves. If we suffer with Him, we shall also reign with Him. For every joyful mystery of the rosary, there is a darker as well as a lighter side. At the Annunciation, Mary "was much perplexed" (Luke 1:29), and it was only after this that peace and happiness followed. The Presentation is a joyful mystery, but the prophecy of Simeon at that time is one of the seven sorrows of Mary. The finding of the Child in the temple was also a joyful event, but it occurred only after Mary suffered the anguish of losing Him.

Pius XII says:

> The life and sufferings of Our Savior, the pains which so many great men have borne and even sought, and through which they have matured and risen to the summits of Christian heroism, the daily example we see

of acceptance of the Cross with resignation: all this reveals the meaning of suffering, of the patient acceptance of pain in the present plan of salvation.[1]

In men's relations with God there has always been, strangely enough, some connection between suffering and happiness. From a heart that had known the heavy weight of sorrow, Joyce Kilmer expressed the beautiful paradox:

> Lo, comfort blooms on pain, and peace on strife,
> and gain on loss!
> What is the key to Everlasting Life?
> A blood-stained Cross.[2]

The Nurse Who Can Help

In the last analysis, there is only one sort of nurse who can effectively help her patient to build up a strong spirit of resignation in great illness, and that is the nurse who is herself truly resigned to whatever suffering God may see fit to send her. "No one gives what he does not possess." Nor is there any clever rule for acquiring resignation. It must be developed by reading and listening and meditating and praying and doing voluntary penance, and cheerfully and lovingly carrying your own cross behind the Cross of Jesus Christ, who was perfectly resigned to the will of His heavenly Father.

He who truly loves is never satisfied unless he can sacrifice for the one he loves. Suffering and death are the noblest and greatest of sacrifices, and willingness to undergo them is characteristic of great and noble love. No nurse can truly say that she loves God unless she is willing to sacrifice for God. And if her love for God is deep enough, she is willing to suffer and die for that love.

The consequences of the Christian teaching on suffering are bewildering, for the most joyous people in the world are those who

[1] Address to members of the medical profession, Rome, January 8, 1956.

[2] Joyce Kilmer, "Pennies" from *Trees and Other Poems*, copyright 1914, by George H. Doran Company. Reprinted by permission of Doubleday & Company, Inc.

eagerly embrace trials. They are the most thoughtful, the kindest, the happiest. It may seem strange to us that God in mapping out our lives chose no other way than this. Yet, the special gift to the followers of Christ, even His own Mother, has always been trials and crosses. It is not a contradiction; it is but one more of Christ's paradoxes and promises fulfilled. Saint John Vianney expressed it this way: "The Cross is the gift that God makes to His friends."[3]

[3] Saint John Vianney, *The Curé of Ars to His People*, St. Meinrad, Ind.: Grail Publications, 1951, p. 89.

(PHOTO BY CHARLES KRISAN.)

CHAPTER 13

Nursing—A Profession and a Vocation

Why are you a nurse? · An understanding heart

A WOMAN HIGHLY ESTEEMED among those in the medical field, well-known throughout the world for her contribution to medicine, and greatly admired for the dedication of her life to the sick and afflicted, confided the inspiration of her life in these words:

> My life is a prayer, day and night, given unreservedly to God. I wake in the morning to place myself at His service and command. I know I am doing His work as He guides me, and gives me the necessary strength, knowledge, patience and inspiration.[1]

These are the words of Sister Elizabeth Kenny. How strongly she expresses her conviction that nursing is not just another job, not just another way to earn a living wage. Too little has been made of the fact that nursing is a vocation in the fullest sense of the word.

"We call it a vocation," says Pius XII, "because the person who embraces the profession of a nurse responds to the call of Christ's charity: 'Come, blessed of my Father.' Christ will say to you on the Day of Judgment, 'I was sick, and you visited me. . . . Whatever you have done for the sickest, you did it for me.' "[2]

Sister Kenny sums up some fundamental qualities which must become living realities in the heart of the ideal twentieth-century nurse:

[1] Sister Elizabeth Kenny, "Pain Has No Frontiers," *Guideposts*, October, 1950, p. 4. Copyright 1950 by Guideposts Associates, Inc. Published at Carmel, N.Y.

[2] Address to members of the nursing profession, Rome, May 26, 1952.

> We are put on this earth for a special destiny. Simply, it is our destiny to do the work of God. Each finds his way to do that work. If we live up to it, all is well here and hereafter. . . . The only satisfactory life is a life of service . . . and perhaps the greatest possible service to humanity is to the sick. . . . There is no profession that so closely follows in the footsteps of Christ than the work of healing.[3]

The nurse who looks upon her profession as a vocation will live in an atmosphere that gives meaning to the problem of pain, that interprets the riddle of suffering, that motivates love for the sick and helps her to realize that they are brothers of the suffering Christ. The crucifix will be an intimate part of her life as an eloquent reminder that no one suffers alone.

Why Are You a Nurse?

The years of training which a nurse must undergo are calculated to equip her to carry on her tasks efficiently and competently. But something more than this is necessary. The "know how" is important, but the "know why" is indispensable. Nursing is more than a profession. It is a vocation, a dedication, a consecration. To the layman, there is something of the glamorous about nursing. But it takes little time for this aspect to fade into obscurity as a young nurse begins her new duties. There will be early risings, all-night vigils, mental cases, cancer victims. Perhaps the thought will flash through your mind that there are easier ways to make a living. But that thought will vanish quickly because this is not just another job. It is your place in Christ's plan. It is your vocation.

God and His world have need of saintly priests and nuns. But God has need, too, for spiritual-minded and saintly physicians and nurses. "Vocation" means God's own choosing of a way of life in which a man will best serve God and neighbor.

A girl becomes a nurse—or should at least—in the last analysis not because of glamor, not because of money, not even merely because she likes the life. She becomes a nurse because God wants her

[3] Sister Elizabeth Kenny, *op. cit.*, p. 22.

to serve Him as a nurse; because she is convinced that nursing is the field where she can best fulfill the will of Christ, serve her neighbor, and in so doing attain a measure of happiness here and eternal happiness hereafter.

You are obeying the call of Christ to take care of His friends, the sick and the suffering and the unfortunate. Anything you do for them is a personal favor to Him.

God has, in His plan, determined a specific way of life and specific tasks for you to accomplish. He could have accomplished these things in some other way or through some other person. But, as a matter of fact, He has chosen you. And each of those daily chores is His will for you. He wants you to do them, and to do them to the very best of your ability. The unpleasant tasks, the irritable patient, the overdemanding visitor, the doctor lacking in understanding—all these are part of your daily work. Such things are not glamorous or heroic in the eyes of the world. But then Christ has not given you a vocation to be glamorous or spectacular.

Your spirit might be summed up in this way:

> This is my work, whatever it may be,
> No other one can do this work but me.
> To others, the nobler task, the braver deed,
> Mine only to fulfill a simpler need.
> Impress this truth upon me—that no one
> Can do the part that I shall leave undone.
> No matter where allotted work may be,
> To do it well is what is asked of me.[4]

Many people feel that they could achieve heroic sanctity if they could do it in the way which appeals to them. They picture themselves giving their life on a battlefield. They envision themselves as martyrs for the Faith. Your task is heroic, but usually not in a striking way. It consists of a sense of humor when everything is going wrong, a friendly gesture, a cheerful word, a radiant smile. It is the giving of what you are as well as what you have.

[4] *Ephpheta*, Brooklyn, N.Y.: Diocesan Apostolate for Deaf, Speechless and Hard of Hearing, January, 1945. Used with permission.

An Understanding Heart

One prayer should be often on your lips: "Give me, O Lord, an understanding heart." Could you, as a nurse, pray for anything more appropriate? Patients at times will take you for granted, and you may be tempted to become overly professional and even callous. You will meet people at their worst. Patients are often demanding and selfish. Never let the human in you predominate over the divine. It is an understanding heart that will see you through your daily difficulties.

You will put drops into the eyes of the newborn and close forever the eyes of the dead. You may never be called upon to serve in a way that the world considers heroic, striking, or newsworthy. Your heroism takes other channels. You are serving Christ in the person of His friends, the sick and the afflicted. You help them to go up their own Calvary. Like Veronica, you soothe their wounds, like the Cyrenian, you help them to bear their cross; like Mary, your presence helps them to endure it. Your understanding heart is their spiritual wonder drug.

If this is the spirit of your vocation, then your cap will crown a head full of wisdom, hands full of healing, and a heart full of understanding. "The Church itself," says Pope Paul VI, "opens wide its arms to you and expresses its blessing and encouragement for your noble mission of study and of therapy."[5]

[5] Address on the occasion of the fiftieth anniversary of the Santa Maria della Pieta Hospital, Dec. 2, 1963.

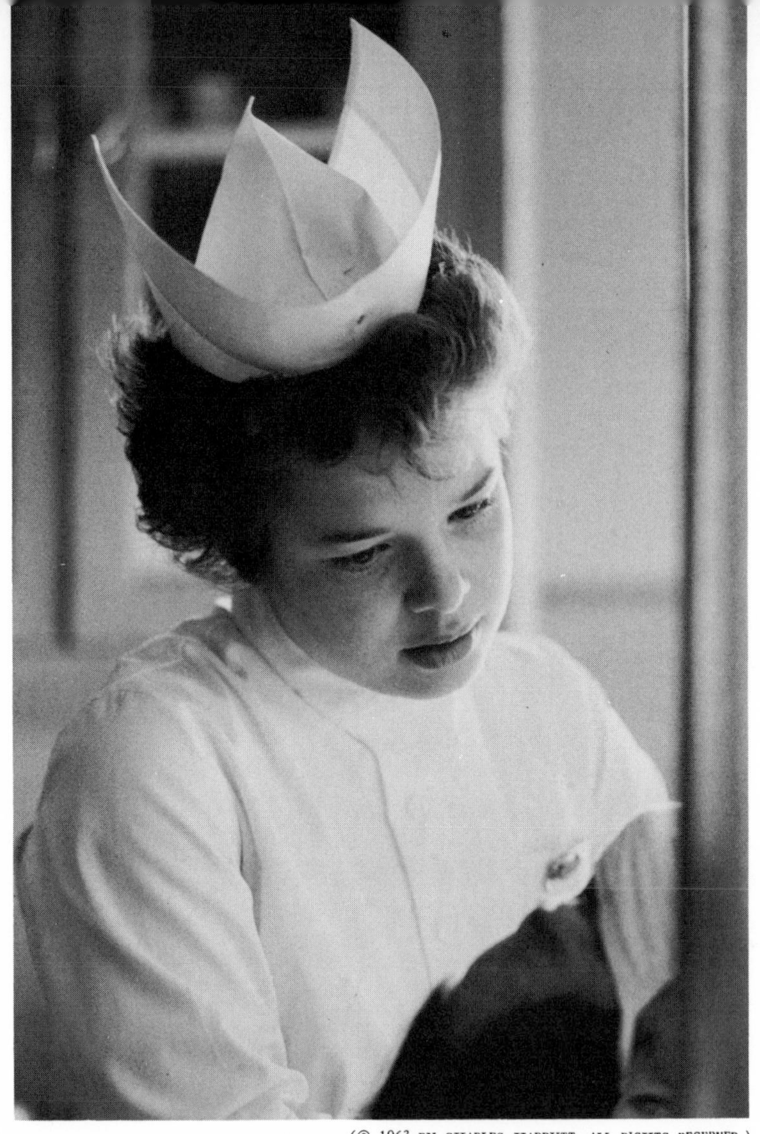

St. Vincent's Hospital, New York.

CHAPTER 14

The Ideal Nurse

Qualities of a nurse

DURING THE COMMUNIST OPPRESSION in China, the persecutors were very much concerned with the eradication of the Legion of Mary. This zealous organization had become the focal point of Catholic action. With Mary as their leader and model, Chinese Catholics presented a solid front against the attacks of the atheists.

Upon the arrest of a Catholic, the Communists would often demand to know the whereabouts of Mary, the leader of the powerful legion. When they were told that she is in heaven, they would accuse the prisoners of lying. They felt that the woman who was the inspiration for such devotion and allegiance could never be that same Mary who first walked the earth two thousand years ago.

Mary has been the most powerful influence—second only to Christ Himself—in the history of Christianity.

It is this woman to whom we point as the ideal of all nurses. The difficult task of living up to the moral laws governing the nursing profession, the development of the many virtues that are necessary in a good nurse, the overcoming of self-love, the acquisition of true Christian charity—these things become easier to attain in direct proportion to a nurse's devotion to Mary as her model.

Mary gave the example of the acceptance of a vocation as the will of God when she humbly submitted to the plan of God as told to her by the Angel Gabriel. She sanctified obstetrical nursing when she hastened to her cousin Elizabeth to assist at the birth of John the Baptist. No pediatric nurse ever attended a child with more loving care than did Mary the Infant Jesus. She gave an example of obedience to civil law by going to Bethlehem, to religious law by going to Jerusalem, to her superior by accompanying Joseph to Egypt. Her kindness and consideration were shown vividly at Cana, when she interceded with Our Lord to obtain wine for the guests at the wedding. Her cheerfulness welled forth from a heart overflowing with the gifts of God.

Her own comfort was always considered last of all as she carried fuel for the fire, drew water from the village well, spun thread, wove cloth, made garments, prepared meals, and performed innumerable duties around the house. Silence was one of her outstanding virtues, for few of her words are related in Scripture. Compassion, which means "suffering with," was so great in Mary that she is referred to as the co-redemptrix with the suffering Redeemer—a wonderful example to a nurse, who will work effectively in proportion to the compassion she has on her patients as brothers and sisters of the suffering Christ. Mary's assistance with Jesus at the deathbed of Saint Joseph was so perfect that Joseph has been declared patron of a happy death. It was around Mary that the apostles rallied when Christ had ascended to His Father, and she cared not only for their spiritual needs but their physical needs as well. To this day, Our Lady pours out her love upon the sick in the miracles that take place in her shrine at Lourdes and in her other shrines in various parts of the world.

Qualities of a Nurse

Just as Mary was given outstanding virtues by the Creator in order that she might fulfill her task on earth, so too the nurse, being destined to do special work, is equipped by Almighty God her Creator with those qualities which she will need to be a good nurse.

> "What shall I give her now?" said God.
> "She has the strength with which to plod
> The ways of life, the love of right,
> The gift of song when skies are bright.
>
> "Wisdom is planted in her mind,
> This girl shall be both true and kind;

Earth's beauty shall delight her eyes
And to its glories she shall rise.

"She shall know right from wrong, and she
Defender of the Faith shall be;
What more on her can I bestow
Before to earth I let her go?"

Then spoke an angel standing near:
"Wisdom is not enough, I fear,
Master, for all that she must do
Grant her a sense of humor, too."[1]

Here is God, surrounded by many of His angels, preparing the nurse's soul for its entrance into the world. A generous share of natural gifts and talents is bestowed upon her. All the supernatural virtues implanted in souls at baptism will be hers. But these are not enough because the nurse's task is not an ordinary one.

An angel comes forward with a lamp, the symbol of nursing, and presents it as a sign that God is calling her to this particular state of life.

A second angel opens a scroll and reads a passage from Scripture that the nurse must keep in mind at all times: "The Lord loves obedience better than any sacrifice" (I Kings 15:22).

The lamp is now filled with oil, which is a figure of strength and healing.

Another angel steps forward with a burning taper and lights the lamp, saying: "Let your light shine before your fellowmen, that they may see your good example and praise your Father who is in heaven" (Matt. 5:16).

Almighty God Himself then points to the flame of the lamp as a symbol of charity and commands that a nurse let the warmth of her charity extend to all men, regardless of their race or station in life. "Whatever you do to one of the least of my brethren, you do to me."

Finally, before the soul sets out upon its journey through life,

[1] Edgar A. Guest, "Sense of Humor," *Collected Verse*, copyrighted 1947. Used with permission.

one of the angels reads God's promise to those nurses who are faithful to their trust: "God Himself shall abide in their midst. He shall wipe away every tear from their eyes. No longer will there be death, no longer will there be mourning or cry of anguish or pain. . . . Night will be no more, and so they will have no need of light of lamp or of sun, because the Lord will shine upon them, and they will reign for ever and ever" (Apoc. 21:3-4; 22:5).

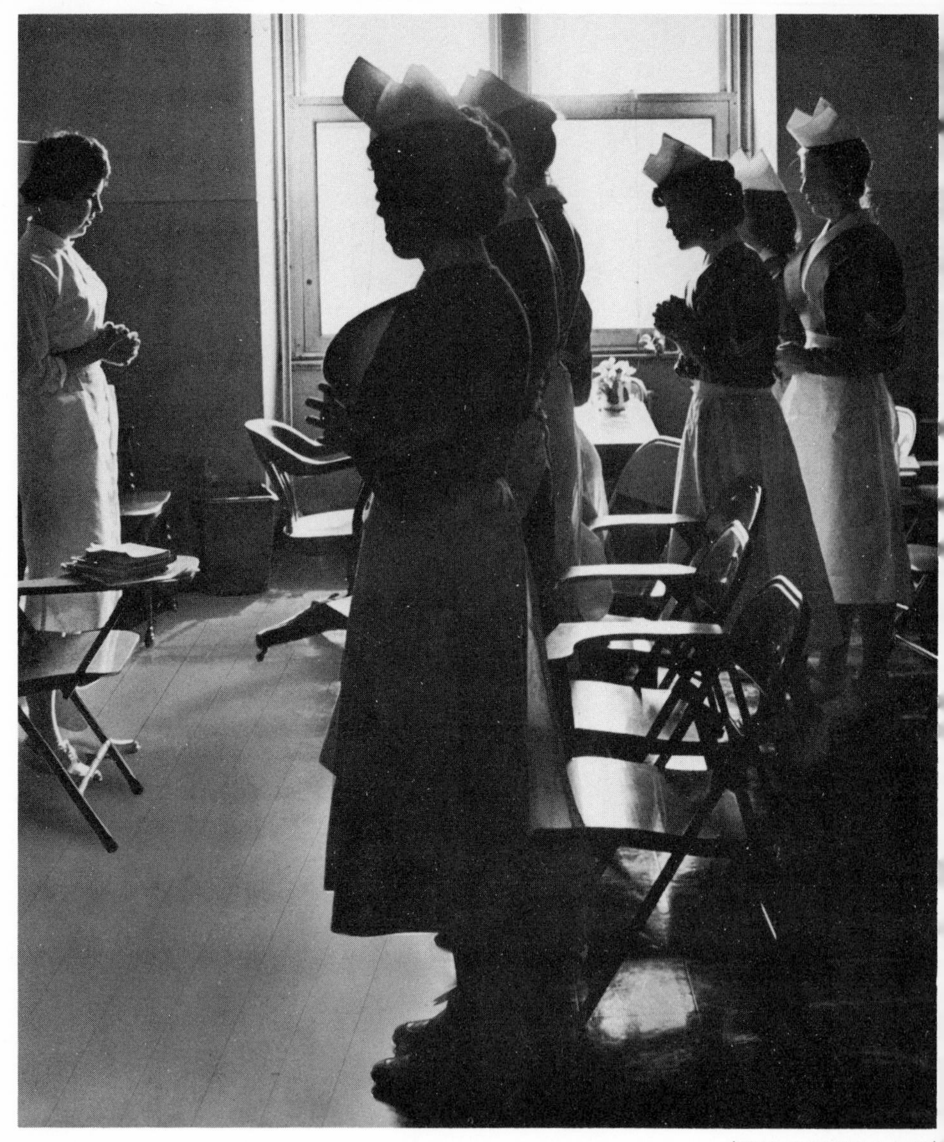

(PHOTO BY MARTIN J. DAIN.)

St. Vincent's Hospital, New York.

CHAPTER 15

The Nurse—A Woman of Prayer

THERE CAN BE NO DOUBT of Christ's particular love for the sick, the afflicted, the helpless. That is why the nurse's vocation is in a special way "Christlike." The standards by which Christ will pass judgment on the last day have a singular application to the life of the nurse. As a nurse fulfills her task of feeding a helpless patient, as she befriends one who is left alone, as she walks the darkened corridor into a dimly lighted room to moisten the parched lips of a patient, she might well recall the words of Christ on the last day: "Come, you that have received a blessing from my Father . . . for I was hungry, and you gave me food, thirsty, and you gave me drink; I was a stranger, and you brought me home, naked, and you clothed me, sick, and you cared for me" (Matt. 25: 34-36).

Because the nurse's vocation is so singularly "Christlike," it is imperative that she work "through Him, and in Him, and with Him." The nurse will find the solution to most of her difficulties, will see her vocation in a new light, through personal contact with Christ. Prayer is that personal contact.

Any nurse who works in pediatrics has one lesson strikingly

brought home to her: the helplessness of infancy. An infant cannot feed himself, cannot help himself, cannot stand up himself. Nature has kept from him all means of solving his own problems—except one, and that is his voice. By crying and screaming, the infant can let those around know of his hunger and can rouse them from sleep if a need arises at night. The voice of the infant effectively brings others to his service to fulfill his needs and to care for him.

The infant is the living counterpart of our soul's relation to God. We are weak and helpless spiritually. God has given us a means by which to gain all the help we need. That means is prayer.

You are called upon by your vocation to work not only with bodies but with souls as well. How can a nurse expect to give anything spiritually unless first of all she herself has something to give? That is another reason why prayer is so important in her life.

A conscientious nurse, in working for the spiritual and physical well-being of her patient, must labor with might and main because nothing less than the best is worthy of God and her calling. Once she has done her best, then she must leave the rest up to God. In a word, a good nurse will be a woman of prayer.

Your never-ending duties on the ward, those inconvenient hospital rules, the tasks carried out at the doctor's bidding—these must never take on the appearance of a crazy quilt or puzzle picture. There must be a symmetry, a unity of plan, a dominant purpose. Prayer will give that purpose, that vital spark, that uplift of mind and heart so necessary in one who wears the nurse's cap.

Dr. Alexis Carrel, the famous surgeon, once declared: "Prayer, our dearest source of power and perfection, has been left miserably undeveloped." The nurse can never be satisfied with accomplishing her tasks on a merely natural level. If she is to live her vocation fully, she must possess the strength that only prayer can give.

Daily Prayers

Prayer in Praise of God

To the King of ages, immortal and invisible, the only God, be honor and glory forever and ever. Amen.

Morning Prayer

Lord God Almighty, Who has brought us to the beginning of this day, protect us by Your power, so that today we may fall into no sin. May our thoughts, words, and actions always begin and be directed according to Your justice. Through Christ Our Lord. Amen.

Dedication to Mary

My Queen! My Mother! I give myself entirely to you. To show my devotion, I consecrate to you this day my eyes, ears, mouth, heart, my entire self. O loving Mother, since I am yours, keep me, defend me, as your property and possession. Amen.

Prayer When Going Off Duty

O God, Who has ordained that there should be a time for play as well as a time for work, deign to bless my free time, that I may ever remain a credit to my profession and my Faith. Through Christ Our Lord. Amen.

Night Prayer

Visit, we beseech You, O Lord, this house, and drive far from it all snares of the devil. Let Your holy angels dwell here to preserve us in peace; and may Your blessing be always upon us. Through Christ Our Lord. Amen.

Confession

Prayer to the Holy Spirit before Confession

O Holy Spirit, enlighten my mind that I may know my sins; inflame my heart with true sorrow; bless my lips that I may confess properly. Make me prompt to obey my confessor as my spiritual superior, and anxious to follow his advice as the physician of my soul. Holy Spirit, so offended by my sins, help me to make a good confession. Amen.

Examination of Conscience

Preliminary Questions

Did I make a good confession the last time?
Did I forget a grievous sin in the last confession?
Have I avoided the proximate occasion of mortal sin?

If I have committed any grievous sins during the time since I made my last good confession, I must now recall them to mind.

If, at this time, I have only venial sins to confess, I might include a mortal sin of one of my former confessions.

The Ten Commandments of God

FIRST COMMANDMENT: I am the Lord thy God; thou shalt not have strange gods before Me.

Have I been disrespectful toward persons, places, or things consecrated to God?

Did I despair of God's mercy?

Did I lack confidence in God in time of trouble or temptation?

Have I been guilty of rebelling against the law of God, His mercy, or His justice?

Have I willfully doubted things revealed by God?

Have I refused to be resigned to God's holy will?

Have I performed my prayers or other religious exercises in a hurried, careless, or distracted manner?

Have I conducted myself irreverently in the presence of God in the Blessed Sacrament?

Have I been ashamed of my religion through human respect?

Have I taken part in non-Catholic services?

Have I been superstitious?

SECOND COMMANDMENT: Thou shalt not take the name of the Lord thy God in vain.

Have I used God's name irreverently?

Have I used profane language?

THIRD COMMANDMENT: Remember thou keep holy the Lord's Day.

Have I performed unnecessary servile work on these days, and how long?

FOURTH COMMANDMENT: Honor thy father and thy mother.

Have I been disrespectful to my superiors? Have I disobeyed them?

Have I been contemptuous of civil law or hospital regulations?

FIFTH COMMANDMENT: Thou shalt not kill.

Am I guilty of eating, or of drinking intoxicating liquor, immoderately?

Have I willfully entertained thoughts of jealousy, aversion, resentment, or contempt of others?

Have I yielded to impatience or irritability in word or deed?

Have I wished evil to my neighbor?

Have I ridiculed or insulted others?

Have I provoked others to anger?

Have I caused the death of a patient directly or indirectly?

Am I guilty of cooperating in euthanasia? Abortion? Immoral operations?

Have I given bad example by conduct unbecoming a nurse?

Have I gravely or slightly neglected my charge?

Have I unnecessarily exposed my own life or health, or that of another, to grave danger?

Have I been careless in the administration of medicines?

Have I been guilty of improper sterilization of instruments?

Have I been careless with poisons, instruments, or other articles with which a patient might injure himself or others?

Have I made narcotics or alcohol available without authorization?

SIXTH COMMANDMENT: Thou shalt not commit adultery.

Have I been true to my marriage partner?

Am I guilty of sinful dancing?

Have I committed impure acts with others or with myself?

Have I sinfully caressed a person to whom I am not married?

Am I guilty of impure speech or looks?

Am I guilty of the sin of contraception?

Have I been the occasion for another's sin by conversation, dress, giving immoral literature, etc.?

Have I exposed a patient's body unnecessarily and immodestly?

Have I instructed others concerning sinful birth control? Suggested it?

SEVENTH COMMANDMENT: Thou shalt not steal.

Have I stolen money?

Have I purchased anything for which I could never pay?

Have I borrowed money and made no effort to repay?

Have I taken things from my place of work?

Did I waste time? Material?

Did I charge exorbitant fees?

Have I violated justice or charity by discriminating against anyone because of race or color?

If I am in an administrative position, am I responsible for the payment of unjust wages?

Have I charged a patient for medication that he did not receive?

EIGHTH COMMANDMENT: Thou shalt not bear false witness against thy neighbor.

Have I told lies which caused injury to my neighbors?

Have I told a lie to spare myself some embarrassment?

Have I judged or suspected others rashly?

Have I willfully entertained unkind thoughts about others? Have I made uncharitable remarks about them?

Have I, without necessity or reason, revealed a secret defect in my neighbor's character?

Have I revealed professional secrets?

Have I falsified charts?

NINTH COMMANDMENT: Thou shalt not covet thy neighbor's wife.

Did I willfully entertain impure thoughts?

Did I give full consent to impure desires?

TENTH COMMANDMENT: Thou shalt not covet thy neighbor's goods.

Have I desired to acquire my neighbor's property unjustly?

Have I schemed to enrich myself unjustly?

Have I dismissed all thought of ever repaying what I owe?

Have I given more thought to money than to the welfare of my immortal soul?

The Six Precepts of the Church

FIRST PRECEPT: To assist at Mass on all Sundays and holydays of obligation.

Have I missed Holy Mass on any Sunday or holyday of obligation?

Did I through my own fault come late to Mass?

SECOND PRECEPT: To fast and to abstain on the days appointed.

Did I violate this precept slightly or in a grave manner?

If I needed a dispensation from the lenten regulations, did I obtain it?

THIRD PRECEPT: To confess our sins at least once a year.

Have I gone to confession during the past year?

FOURTH PRECEPT: To receive Holy Communion during the Easter time.

Did I fulfill my Easter duty?

FIFTH PRECEPT: To contribute to the support of the Church.

Have I neglected to contribute my just share of financial help to my parish church?

SIXTH PRECEPT: To observe the laws of the Church concerning marriage.

Did I act as a witness at a non-Catholic marriage?

Did I help or encourage any Catholic to marry outside the Church?

An Act of Contrition

O my God, I am heartily sorry for having offended Thee, and I detest all my sins, because of Thy just punishments, but most of all because they offend Thee, my God, Who are all-good and deserving of all my love. I firmly resolve, with the help of Thy grace, to sin no more and to avoid the near occasions of sin.

Prayer after Confession

Accept, O Lord Jesus, my humble thanks for Your merciful forgiveness. Accept my promise to avoid sin and its occasions in the future. Bless the priest who gave me absolution in Your Name, and bring me safely through this sinful world into Your eternal kingdom. Amen.

Prayers for Various Occasions

Prayer to Our Lady before Communion

O Blessed Mother of God, who prepared so well and so lovingly for the birth of Jesus, obtain for me from God the grace to excite in my heart an ardent love for your divine Son, that I may worthily receive Him in the Holy Sacrament of the Altar. Amen.

Prayer after Communion

Dearest Lord, I thank You for coming into my heart. Make me a good nurse. I love You and will try always to please You. Amen.

Surrender of Self

Receive, O Lord, all my liberty. Accept my memory, my intellect, and my entire will. Whatever I have or possess, You have given to me; I return it all to You to dispose of as You will. Give me only Your love and Your grace and I am rich, filled, with no need to seek further.

Prayer in Time of Trial

O God, our refuge and our strength, mercifully look down on me as I cry to You, and turn away the scourges of Your anger, which I justly deserve for my sins. Through Christ Our Lord. Amen.

Prayer for Purity

Immaculate Virgin Mary, who combined an ardent love of Saint Joseph with perfect purity, obtain for me the grace to imitate you, so that I may some day share with you the reward that your divine Son has promised to the clean of heart. Through Christ Our Lord. Amen.

Prayer of Thanksgiving

O God, Whose mercies are without number, and Whose treasure of goodness is infinite, we give thanks to Your most gracious Majesty for Your many gifts. We continue to beg Your forbearance, so that just as You have granted our past requests, however undeserving we have been, You may one day grant us the great gift of eternal life. Through Christ Our Lord. Amen.

Act of Resignation to Death

O Lord, my God, from this day I accept from Your Hand, willingly and with submission, the kind of death that it may please You to send me, with all its sorrows, pains, and anguish. Amen.

Prayer for the Church

Listen, in Your clemency, we beseech You, O Lord, to the prayers of Your Church. Bring to naught all the assaults of her enemies; put an end to all false teachings; and enable her to serve You in freedom and in safety. Amen.

Prayer for Priests

O dearest Jesus! Look down with love on Your priests; fill them with burning zeal for the conversion of sinners; keep unstained their anointed hands which daily touch Your Immaculate Body; keep unsullied their lips purpled with Your Precious Blood; keep pure and unearthly a heart sealed with the sublime marks of Your glorious priesthood; bless their labors with abundant fruit, and may those to whom they have ministered on earth be one day their joy and consolation in heaven. Amen.

Prayer When the Church Is Persecuted

Graciously accept, O Lord, the prayers of Your Church, that enemies having been put to flight, and false teachings wiped out, we may serve You in safety and freedom. Amen.

Prayer for Our Country[1]

Almighty God, we make our earnest prayer that You will keep our country in Your holy protection; that You will save it from all enemies

[1] Adapted from the inaugural prayer of George Washington.

at home and abroad; that You will incline the hearts of the citizens to cultivate a spirit of subordination and obedience to government, and entertain a brotherly affection and love for one another, and for their fellow citizens of the nation at large. And, finally, that You will most graciously be pleased to dispose us all to do justice, to love mercy, and to conduct ourselves with charity, humility, and pacific temper of mind, which were the characteristics of the Divine Author of our blessed religion, and without a humble imitation of Whose example in these things we can never hope to be a happy nation. Grant our supplication, we beseech You, through Jesus Christ Our Lord. Amen.

Prayer for Peace

O God, the Author of holy desires, correct advice, and just works, grant to Your servants that peace which the world is not able to give, so that our hearts being devoted to Your laws, and the fear of enemies being put aside, our days by Your protection may be peaceful. Through Christ Our Lord. Amen.

Prayer for the Tempted

O God, Who makes the wicked just, and does not will the death of the sinner, protect by Your heavenly help Your servants who rely on Your mercy, and preserve them by Your constant protection, that they may serve You faithfully, and not be separated from You by any temptation. Amen.

Prayer for Relatives and Friends

O God, Who by the grace of the Holy Spirit has infused charity into the hearts of the faithful, have mercy on our relatives and friends. Grant them health of mind and body. May they love You ardently, and always do those things which are pleasing to You. Through Christ Our Lord. Amen.

Prayer for Benefactors

May it please You, O Lord, to reward with eternal life all those who do good to us for Your Name's sake. Amen.

Prayer in Honor of Saint Luke for Doctors

Good Saint Luke, who combined a physician's knowledge with faith in Jesus and love for His Mother, obtain for doctors great medical skill, lively divine faith, and a spirit of kindliness and charity. Through Christ Our Lord. Amen.

Prayer for a Charge Nurse

Almighty and Eternal God, the Author and Giver of all true authority, grant my superior the grace to fulfill her duties with prudence, justice, and charity, and grant me the grace to bear with her human failings and to carry out her directions obediently to the best of my ability. Through Christ Our Lord. Amen.

Prayer of a Student to the Sacred Heart

Make me, O Lord, quick to learn, cheerful to obey, humble to take correction, and resigned in all my trials. Make me a nurse pleasing to Your Sacred Heart, and unite me with You one day in Your eternal kingdom. Amen.

Prayer of a Charge Nurse

O Lord Jesus Christ, Who perfectly combined divine authority with humility and kindness, help me to exercise my office with efficiency and with a constant spirit of Christian love. Amen.

Prayer of a Nurse in Military Service

Almighty and Eternal God, Whose Church is like an army set in array, grant that I, who wear the military uniform, may never fail to be a good soldier of Jesus Christ and, having nursed the sick and the wounded with true Christian charity, may be united at last with You in my eternal country. Amen.

Prayer in Honor of Saint Camillus

O God, Who gave Saint Camillus the grace to nurse the sick with true Christian charity, grant through his intercession that I may do my nursing in a manner pleasing to You, and so merit an eternal reward. Through Christ Our Lord. Amen.

Prayer before Assisting at an Operation

Grant, I beseech You, O Lord, that as I approach my work with clean hands, I may also, through Your merciful forgiveness, approach it with a pure soul. Give alertness to my mind, skill to my fingers, and patience to my heart. Amen.

Prayer for a Newborn

O Holy Infant Jesus, Lover of children, bless this little infant newly born into the world. Strengthen his (her) body by Your power; and in Your loving kindness refresh his (her) soul by the saving waters of baptism, that he (she) may be destined for an eternal union with You. Amen.

Prayer for a Sick Child

Father of mercies and God of all consolation, Who pours forth Your healing grace on bodies as well as souls, deign to raise up this sick child and restore him (her) to Your Holy Church and to his (her) parents, so that his (her) life being prolonged, advancing in grace and wisdom before You and before men, he (she) may serve You in justice and holiness, and express due gratitude for Your mercy. Through Christ Our Lord. Amen.

Prayer for a Sick Person

O Holy Lord, Father Almighty, Eternal God, pour out Your gracious blessing upon the sick. Graciously draw near at the invocation of Your name, so that, having freed Your servant from sickness and having given him (her) health, You may raise him (her) up by Your right hand, strengthen him (her) by Your power, and restore him (her) to Your Holy Church. Amen.

Prayer for All the Sick

O God of the heavenly virtues, Who drives all sickness and all infirmity from the bodies of men by the power of Your word, graciously draw near to Your sick servants, that with weakness put to flight, and health and strength continually renewed, they may ever bless Your Holy Name. Amen.

Prayer to Be Said by a Sick Person

My God, I believe in You, I hope in You, I love You above all things with all my soul, with all my heart, and with all my strength. I love You because You are infinitely good and worthy of being loved; and because I love You, I repent with all my heart of having offended You. Have mercy on me, a sinner. Amen.

Prayer for a Patient Who Has Received Communion

O Holy Lord, Father Almighty, Eternal God, we earnestly beseech You that the most Sacred Body of Our Lord Jesus Christ, Your Son, which our brother (sister) has received, may be an eternal remedy for him (her) both in body and soul. Amen.

Prayer for a Patient Who Has Received Extreme Unction

Lord God, You have spoken through Your Apostle, James, saying: "Is anyone of you sick? He should call in the priests of the Church, and have them pray over him, while they anoint him with oil in the name of the Lord. That prayer, said with faith, will save the sick person, and the Lord will restore him to health. If he has committed sins, they will be forgiven him." We beseech You, our Redeemer, to cure by the grace of the Holy Spirit the ailments of this sick man (woman). Heal his (her) wounds, and forgive his (her) sins. Alleviate all his (her) physical and mental sufferings, and mercifully restore him (her) to good health, so that, having recovered through Your mercy, he (she) may return to his (her) former duties. Amen.

Prayer for a Patient in Imminent Danger of Death

O most gracious God, Father of mercies, and God of all consolation, Who wills that no one should perish who believes and trusts in You, in Your great mercy, look kindly upon Your servant whom true faith and Christian hope commend to You. Visit him (her) with Your saving power, and through the passion and death of Your Only Begotten Son graciously grant to him (her) pardon and remission of all his (her) sins. May his (her) soul at the hour of its departure find You a merciful Judge. Cleansed from every stain by the Blood of Your Son, may he (she) be worthy to pass into life everlasting. Through Christ Our Lord. Amen.

Prayer for All the Dying

O most merciful Jesus, Lover of souls, I pray You, by the agony of Your most Sacred Heart, and by the sorrows of Your Immaculate Mother, cleanse in Your own Blood the sinners of the whole world who are now in their agony and who are to die this day. Amen.

Heart of Jesus, once in agony, pity the dying. Amen.

The Litany for the Dying

Lord, have mercy.
Christ, have mercy.
Lord, have mercy.
Holy Mary, pray for him (her).
All you holy angels and archangels, pray for him (her).
Holy Abel, pray for him (her).
All you choirs of the just, pray for him (her).
Holy Abraham, pray for him (her).
St. John the Baptist, pray for him (her).
St. Joseph, pray for him (her).
All you holy patriarchs and prophets, pray for him (her).
St. Peter, pray for him (her).
St. Paul, pray for him (her).
St. Andrew, pray for him (her).
St. John, pray for him (her).
All you holy apostles and evangelists, pray for him (her).
All you holy disciples of Our Lord, pray for him (her).
All you holy Innocents, pray for him (her).

St. Stephen, pray for him (her).
St. Lawrence, pray for him (her).
All you holy martyrs, pray for him (her).
St. Sylvester, pray for him (her).
St. Gregory, pray for him (her).
St. Augustine, pray for him (her).
All you holy bishops and confessors, pray for him (her).
St. Benedict, pray for him (her).
St. Francis, pray for him (her).
St. Camillus, pray for him (her).
St. John of God, pray for him (her).
All you holy monks and hermits, pray for him (her).
St. Mary Magdalen, pray for him (her).
St. Lucy, pray for him (her).
All you holy virgins and widows, pray for him (her).
All you holy saints of God, intercede for him (her).
Be merciful, spare him (her), O Lord!
Be merciful, deliver him (her), O Lord!
Be merciful, deliver him (her), O Lord!
From Thy anger, deliver him (her), O Lord!
From death's dangers, deliver him (her), O Lord!
From an unholy death, deliver him (her), O Lord!
From the punishments of hell, deliver him (her), O Lord!
From every evil, deliver him (her), O Lord!
From the power of the devil, deliver him (her), O Lord!
Through Thy birth, deliver him (her), O Lord!
Through Thy cross and passion, deliver him (her), O Lord!
Through Thy death and burial, deliver him (her), O Lord!
Through Thy glorious resurrection, deliver him (her), O Lord!
Through Thy wonderful ascension, deliver him (her), O Lord!
Through the grace of the Holy Spirit, the Consoler, deliver him (her), O Lord!
In the day of judgment, deliver him (her), O Lord!
We who are sinners, we implore Thee, hear us.
That Thou wouldst spare him (her), we implore Thee, hear us.
Lord, have mercy.
Christ, have mercy.
Lord, have mercy.

Let Us Pray.

To you do I turn for refuge, St. Joseph, Patron of the dying, at whose happy deathbed Jesus and Mary stood watch. Because of this twofold pledge of hope, I earnestly commend to you the soul of this servant, in his (her) last agony; so that he (she) may, with you as protector, be set free from the snares of the devil and from everlasting death, and may attain to everlasting joy. Through Christ Our Lord. Amen.

My Daily Prayer (Prayer to Be Said by Dying Non-Catholics)

I believe in one God. I believe that God rewards the good and punishes the wicked.

I believe that in God there are three Divine Persons—God the Father, God the Son, and God the Holy Spirit.

I believe that God the Son became Man, without ceasing to be God. I believe that He is my Lord and my Saviour, the Redeemer of the human race, that He died on the Cross for the salvation of all men, that He died also for me.

I believe, on God's authority, everything that He has taught and revealed.

O my God, give me strong faith. O my God, help me to believe with lively faith.

O my God, Who art all-good and all-merciful, I sincerely hope to be saved. Help me to do all that is necessary for my salvation.

I have committed many sins in my life, but now I turn away from them and hate them. I am sorry, truly sorry for all of them, because I have offended Thee, my God, Who art all-good, all-perfect, all-holy, all-merciful and kind, and Who died on the Cross for me.

I love Thee, O my God, with all my heart. Please forgive me for having offended Thee.

I promise, O God, that with Thy help I will never offend Thee again. My God, have mercy on me.

Prayer to the Holy Trinity

Most Holy Trinity, Godhead indivisible, Father, Son, and Holy Spirit, our first beginning and our last end, since You have made us after Your own image and likeness, grant that all the thoughts of our minds, all the words of our tongues, all the affections of our hearts and all our actions may be always conformed to Your most holy will, to the end that after having seen You here below in appearances and in a dark manner by the means of faith, we may come at last to see You face-to-face and possess You perfectly forever in paradise. Amen.

Medical Glossary

ABORTION Termination of a pregnancy before viability.

ABRUPTIO PLACENTAE Premature separation of the placenta.

ABSTINENCE Refraining from the use of the sex faculty, as in the rhythm method of family limitation.

AMNIOTIC FLUID Fluid which surrounds the fetus in utero. (Also *liquor amnii.*)

AMPUTATE To remove; to cut off.

ANOMALY Deviation from the normal.

APNEA Cessation of respiration.

ARTIFICIAL INSEMINATION The injection of semen into the vagina by artificial means.

BAG OF WATERS The amniotic sac and fluid which serve during pregnancy to protect the fetus.

CEPHALIC Pertaining to the head.

CEPHALOTRIPSY Crushing of the fetal head.

CEREBROVASCULAR ACCIDENT Stroke.

CERVIX OF THE UTERUS The neck of the uterus.

CHOLECYSTECTOMY Excision of the gallbladder and cystic duct.

CIRCUMCISION Removal of the end of the prepuce.

COMA An abnormally deep sleep from which the patient cannot be aroused.

CORDOTOMY Spinal cord section of the lateral pathways to relieve pain. (Also *chordotomy.*)

CORNEA Clear, transparent, anterior portion of the eye.

CURETTAGE Scraping of the interior of a cavity.

DECAPITATION Separation of the head from the body.

DECOMPOSITION Decay.

DILATATION AND CURETTAGE The widening of the cervical os with instruments and scraping of the uterine cavity.

DOUCHE A stream of fluid directed into a body cavity.

ECLAMPSIA A toxic complication of pregnancy characterized by convulsions.

-ECTOMY (suffix) To cut out, remove.

ECTOPIC PREGNANCY Extrauterine pregnancy.

EMBOLISM Obstruction of a blood vessel; may be due to clot, air, or any foreign matter.

EMBRYO The product of conception in its earliest stage.

ENDOMETRIUM Mucous membrane lining of the uterus.

EUTHANASIA Mercy killing.

EVISCERATION 1. Protrusion of viscera through the body wall.
2. Removal of several viscera.

EXPIRATION Death.

EXSANGUINATION Radical draining of blood.

EXTRA- (prefix) Outside of.

FALLOPIAN TUBES Oviducts.

FETUS Infant in utero.

FORESKIN The prepuce, covering the glans penis.

GASTRIC LAVAGE Washing out the stomach.

GESTATION Pregnancy.

HEMORRHAGE Bleeding.

HYDATIDIFORM MOLE Cystic proliferation of chorionic villi.

HYDRAMNIOS Excessive production of amniotic fluid. (Also *hydramnion* and *polyhydramnios*.)

HYPEREMESIS GRAVIDARUM Excessive vomiting in pregnancy.

HYPERTENSION Excessive tension, usually synonymous with high blood pressure.

HYPERTROPHY Enlargement of an organ or structure.

HYSTERECTOMY Removal of the uterus.

IMPOTENCY Inability to perform the sex act.

INTRA- (prefix) Within.

LAPAROTOMY Surgical incision into the abdomen.

LIGATE To tie off.

LIGATION The act of tying off a vessel, tube, etc.

MACERATED Putrefied, decomposed.

MENOPAUSE Cessation of menstruation.

MENORRHAGIA Profuse menstrual flow.
MENSTRUATION Menses.
MISCARRIAGE Accidental abortion.
MONSTROSITY A malformed fetus.
NARCOTIC A sleep-producing, pain-relieving drug.
NEPHRITIS Inflammation of a kidney.
NON- (prefix) Not.
ONANISM Withdrawal, a method of contraception.
OOPHORECTOMY Removal of an ovary.
ORCHIDECTOMY Removal of testicle. (Also *orchiectomy.*)
OS The mouth of an organ.
-OSTOMY (suffix) Opening.
-OTOMY (suffix) Cutting into.
OVARY The female gland in which the eggs are developed.
OVUM The egg.
PATHOLOGIC Diseased. (Also *pathological.*)
PENIS Male organ of copulation.
PERITONITIS Inflammation of the peritoneum.
PERNICIOUS VOMITING Hyperemesis gravidarum.
PLACENTA Afterbirth.
PROGNOSIS Probable outcome.
PROSTATE A male gland which secretes a fluid which forms part of the semen.
PULMONARY Pertaining to the lungs.
RENAL Pertaining to the kidneys.
RESUSCITATE To restore respiration.
SALPINGECTOMY Removal of fallopian tube.
SECUNDINES Afterbirth and membranes.
SEMEN Product of prostate and bulbourethral glands, carrying spermatozoa.
SEPSIS Infection.
SPERM Mature male germ cell. (Also *seed.*)
STENOSIS A narrowing or stricture.
STERILITY Inability to reproduce.
TESTICLE Male organ lying within the scrotum which produces spermatozoa.
TOXEMIA Presence of toxin or poison in the blood.
TOXEMIA OF PREGNANCY Toxic state in pregnancy, which ends when pregnancy ends; may be complicated by eclampsia.
TRAUMA Injury.
TUBE See FALLOPIAN TUBE.

UTERUS The hollow, muscular female organ of reproduction in which the fetus develops during pregnancy.

VAGINA Birth canal.

VAS DEFERENS Excretory duct of the testis.

VERNIX CASEOSA Cheeselike covering on skin of fetus and newborn child.

VIABILITY The ability of the fetus to live outside the uterus.

WOMB Uterus.

Theological Glossary

ABSTINENCE Refraining from eating meat, as on Friday. (See FAST.)

BAPTISM The sacrament which makes a man a member of the Church and capable of attaining salvation.

BLESSED SACRAMENT The sacrament of the Eucharist, popularly called "Holy Communion."

BLESSING The calling down of God's special help upon a person or thing. In the case of a priest's blessing, the call to God is sent up officially in the name of the Church.

CHRISTIAN BURIAL Interment in consecrated ground.

COMMUNION The receiving of Jesus Christ under the appearance of bread.

CONFESSION The telling of sins to an authorized priest for the purpose of obtaining forgiveness.

CONFIRMATION The sacrament that makes a Christian a soldier of Jesus Christ.

CONTRITION, ACT OF A prayer expressing sorrow for sin.

EUCHARIST A term equivalent to "Holy Communion" in popular usage.

EXTREME UNCTION The sacrament given to those in danger of death.

FAITH, ACT OF A prayer expressing belief in God and His revelation.

FAST, PENITENTIAL Refraining, according to prescribed norms, from eating the usual amount of food, as during Lent. (See ABSTINENCE.)

FORM The words used in the administration of a sacrament, as opposed to the matter.

HOLY COMMUNION The receiving of Jesus Christ under the appearance of bread.

HOPE, ACT OF A prayer expressing trust in God and His promises.

LAST BLESSING A special blessing given to those in extremis.

LAST RITES The various spiritual ministrations given to Catholics in danger of death.

MATTER The material or external sign of a sacrament, as opposed to the form; such as water, the outward sign of baptism.

MORAL OBLIGATION A duty flowing from the moral law.

MORTAL SIN Serious sin. Grave sin.

OLD LAW The Old Testament, under which the chosen people of God lived prior to the coming of Christ.

PHILOSOPHY One's concept of the correct meaning, goal, and way of life, as seen by the light of reason.

PRECIOUS BLOOD, THE The Blood of Christ.

PRIEST A man taken from among men and ordained for the things that pertain to God.

RELIGION The relationship between God and man.

REVELATION God's direct communication with man.

ROSARY A special prayer to the Virgin Mary, said with beads.

SACRAMENT An external sign instituted by Christ to give grace.

SALVATION Attaining to the eternal reward of heaven.

THEOLOGY The science which is concerned with God and the things of God.

TRADITION The truths of Christian revelation not written in the Bible ("objective divine tradition"); the transmission of Christian revelation through the teaching authority of the Church ("active tradition").

VENIAL SIN Slight sin.

VIATICUM Communion given to a person in danger of death.

VOCATION God's call to a particular state of life.

Bibliography

Aikens, C. *Studies in Ethics for Nurses*, Philadelphia: W. B. Saunders Company, 1938.

Arnold, F. *Are "Mercy-Killings" Justifiable?* (pamphlet), Huntington, Ind.: Our Sunday Visitor Press, 1938.

Barry, D. "Providing Sacraments for Catholics in Non-Catholic Hospitals," *American Ecclesiastical Review*, February, 1934.

Beck, Sister Mary Berenice *Handmaid of the Divine Physician*, Milwaukee: The Bruce Publishing Company, 1952.

Bonnar, A. *The Catholic Doctor*, London: Burns, Oates and Washbourne, Ltd., 1952.

Bourke, V. J. *Ethics: A Textbook in Moral Philosophy*, New York: The Macmillan Company, 1953.

Bouscaren, T. *Ethics of Ectopic Operations*, Milwaukee: The Bruce Publishing Company, 1944.

Bowdern, W. S. *The Catholic Nurse and the Dying* (pamphlet), St. Louis: The Queen's Work, 1934.

Breviarium Romanum.

Brogan, J. *Ethical Principles for the Character of a Nurse*, Milwaukee: The Bruce Publishing Company, 1924.

Carroll, M. G. (translator) *New Problems in Medical Ethics*, edited by P. Flood, Westminster, Md.: The Newman Press, 1953.

Clifford, J. "Sterility Tests and Their Morality," *American Ecclesiastical Review*, November, 1942.

Codex Iuris Canonici.

Connell, F. "Curettage of the Pregnant Uterus during Severe Hemorrhage," *American Ecclesiastical Review*, March, 1944.

——— "Artificial Insemination," *American Ecclesiastical Review*, February, 1945.

——— "Administration of Baptism to Unknown Dying Persons," *American Ecclesiastical Review*, May, 1945.

——— "Anesthesia of a Dying Person," *American Ecclesiastical Review*, September, 1946.

——— "The Removal of a Healthy Appendix," *American Ecclesiastical Review*, June, 1947.

——— *Morals in Politics and Professions*, Westminster, Md.: Newman Press, 1951.

——— "The Rh Factor and Rhythm," *American Ecclesiastical Review*, April, 1952.

——— *Father Connell Answers Moral Questions*, Washington, D.C.: Catholic University of America Press, 1959.

Cunningham, B. *The Morality of Organic Transplantation*, Washington, D.C.: Catholic University, 1944.

Curtis, W. W. *Call The Priest!* (pamphlet), New York: The Catholic Information Society, 1947.

Davis, H. "A Medico-Moral Problem—Ectopic Gestation," *American Ecclesiastical Review*, February, 1942.

——— *Moral and Pastoral Theology*, London: Sheed and Ward, Ltd., 1945. 4 v.

Davis, M. E., and Sheckler, C. E. *DeLee's Obstetrics for Nurses*, 15th ed., Philadelphia: W. B. Saunders Company, 1951.

Donovan, J. "The Use of a Douche after Criminal Attack," *Homiletic and Pastoral Review*, August, 1941.

Dooley, E. A. *An Alphabet for Nurses* (pamphlet), Glen Rock, N.J.: The Paulist Press, 1951.

Doyle, J. B. "The Role of the Gynecologist," *The Linacre Quarterly*, May, 1954.

Farrell, W. *A Companion to the Summa*, New York: Sheed and Ward, 1952.

Ficarra, B. J. *Emergency Surgery*, Philadelphia: F. A. Davis Company, 1953.

Fink, L. "Catholic Ethical Nursing," *Graduate Nurses*, New York, 1939.

Finney, P. *Moral Problems in Hospital Practice*, St. Louis and London: B. Herder Book Company, 1956.

Flood, P. *New Problems in Medical Ethics*, Westminster, Md.: The Newman Press, 1960.

Ford, J. C., and Kelly, G. *Contemporary Moral Theology*, Westminster, Md.: The Newman Press, 1960.

Gillis, J. M. *So Near Is God*, New York: Charles Scribner's Sons, 1953.

Good, F., and Kelly, O. *Marriage, Morals and Medical Ethics*, New York: P. J. Kenedy and Sons, 1951.

Guchteneere, R. *Judgement on Birth Control*, New York: The Macmillan Company, 1931.

Gumpel, P. "Unbaptized Infants: May They Be Saved?" *Downside Review*, Bath, England: Downside Abbey, Autumn, 1954.

Hayes, E. J.; Hayes, P. J.; and Kelly, D. E. *Moral Handbook of Nursing*, New York: The Macmillan Company, 1957.

Hayes, E. J., and Hayes, P. J. *Three Keys to Happiness*, New York: Society of St. Paul, 1952.

——— *Love for a Lifetime*, New York: Society of St. Paul, 1955.

Healy, E. F. *Medical Ethics*, Chicago: Loyola University Press, 1956.

——— *Moral Guidance*, Chicago: Loyola University Press, 1960.

Johnson, B. D. *The Catholic Nurse*, London: Burns, Oates and Washbourne, Ltd., 1950.

Jone, H., and Adelman, U. *Moral Theology*, Westminster, Md.: The Newman Press, 1953.

Kaump, D. K. "The Rh Factor in Hemolytic Disease of the Newborn," *The Linacre Quarterly*, January, 1947.

Kelly, G. "The Morality of Artificial Fecundation," *American Ecclesiastical Review*, August, 1939.

——— "The Moral Aspects of Artificial Insemination," *The Linacre Quarterly*, January, 1947.

——— "Artificial Insemination," *Theological Studies*, March, 1947.

——— "Organic Transplantation," *Theological Studies*, March, 1947.

——— "The Safe Period Method," *Theological Studies*, March, 1947.

——— "Suppression of Ovarian Function to Prevent Metastasis," *Hospital Progress*, April, 1948.

——— "Disposal of Amputated Members," *Hospital Progress*, May, 1948.

——— "Direct and Indirect Abortion," *Hospital Progress*, October, 1948.

——— "An Instruction on Baptism," *Hospital Progress*, February, 1949.

——— *Medico-Moral Problems*, St. Louis: The Catholic Hospital Association of America and Canada, 1949.

——— *Code of Ethics and Religious Directives for Catholic Hospitals*, St. Louis: The Catholic Hospital Association of America and Canada, 1957.

Kenny, Elizabeth "Pain Has No Frontiers," *Guideposts*, New York: Guideposts Associates Inc., October, 1950.

Kenny, J. P. *Principles of Medical Ethics*, Westminster, Md.: The Newman Press, 1962.

Kleist, J., and Lilly, J. (translators) *The New Testament Rendered from the Original Greek*, Milwaukee: The Bruce Publishing Company, 1954.

La Rochelle, S., and Fink, C. *Handbook of Medical Ethics*, Westminster, Md.: The Newman Press, 1943.

Latz, L. J., and Reiner, J. "Natural Conception Control," *Journal of the American Medical Association*, October 19, 1935.

——— "Failures in Natural Conception Control and Their Causes," *Illinois Medical Journal*, March, 1937.

——— "Further Studies on the Sterile and Fertile Periods in Women," *American Journal of Obstetrics and Gynecology*, January, 1942.

Lucey, R. *Artificial Birth Control* (pamphlet), Brooklyn: Catholic Truth Society, 1935.

Lynch, J. J. "Some Moral Phases of Infertility Problems," *The Linacre Quarterly*, May, 1954.

Magonet, A. P. *Hypnosis in Medicine*, London: William Heinemann Medical Books, Ltd., 1952.

Mahoney, E. "Therapeutic Abortion," *The Clergy Review*, London, June, 1938.

Markham, R. J. *Apostolate to Assist Dying Non-Catholics* (pamphlet), Cincinnati: Apostolate to Aid the Dying, 1944.

Marmer, M. J. *Hypnosis in Anesthesiology*, Springfield, Ill.: Charles C Thomas, 1959.

McAllister, J. *Emergency Baptism* (pamphlet), Milwaukee: The Bruce Publishing Company, 1944.

——— *Ethics: with Special Application to the Nursing Profession*, Philadelphia: W. B. Saunders Company, 1947.

——— *Catholicism and Some Moral Problems in Obstetric Nursing* (pamphlet), Washington, D.C.: The National Council of Catholic Nurses, 1953.

McCarthy, J. "The Morality of Artificial Insemination," *The Irish Ecclesiastical Record*, May, 1946.

——— "Censure and the Crime of Abortion," *The Irish Ecclesiastical Record*, November, 1947.

McFadden, C. J. *Medical Ethics*, 5th ed., Philadelphia: F. A. Davis Company, 1961.

McHugh, J. "Canonical Penalties for Abortion," *Homiletic and Pastoral Review*, February, 1934.

Merck Manual of Diagnosis and Therapy, 8th ed., Rahway: Merck and Company, Inc., 1960.

Miller, D. F. *Sick Room Guide* (pamphlet), Liguori, Mo.: The Liguorian Pamphlet Office, 1945.
——— *Blessings in Illness*, Liguori, Mo.: The Liguorian Pamphlet Office, 1951.
Missale Romanum.
Missett, L. *The Ideal Nurse*, Huntington, Ind.: Our Sunday Visitor Press, 1953.
Noldin, H. *Summa Theologiae Moralis*, Ratisbon: Frederick Pustet, 1937.
O'Connell, J. "On the Erection of 'Safe Period' Clinics," *American Ecclesiastical Review*, September, 1939.
O'Donnell, R. "Contraception and Rhythm," *The Nebraska Medical Journal*, April, 1937.
O'Donnell, T. J. *Morals in Medicine*, Westminster, Md.: The Newman Press, 1956.
O'Malley, J. "Assistance of Nurses at Illicit Operations," *Homiletic and Pastoral Review*, October, 1942.
Ostler, D. *Manual for Nurses*, Paterson N.J.: St. Anthony Guild Press, 1939.
Pope Pius XI. *Christian Marriage* (encyclical), Glen Rock, N.J.: The Paulist Press, 1941.
Pope Pius XII. *Moral Questions Affecting Married Life*, Glen Rock, N.J.: The Paulist Press, 1951.
Purvis, M. "Detection of Ovulation by the Basal Temperature Curve," *American Journal of Obstetrics and Gynecology*, July, 1943.
Raccolta, New York: Benziger Bros., 1943.
Regan, R. *Professional Secrecy in the Light of Moral Principles*, Washington, D.C.: Augustinian College, 1943.
Rickaby, J. *Moral Philosophy*, New York: Longmans, Green and Company, Inc., 1929.
Rituale Romanum.
Rumble, L., and Carty, C. *Quizzes on Hospital Ethics*, St. Paul, Minn.: Radio Replies Press, August, 1946.
Ryan, J. *Family Limitation*, New York: Sheed and Ward, 1956.
Sava, A. F. *A Doctor's View of Birth Control* (pamphlet), Paterson, N.J.: St. Anthony's Guild, 1948.
Schlueter, E. "Medical Aspects of Ectopic Gestation," *American Ecclesiastical Review*, August, 1941.
Schwitalla, A. "The American Medical Association and Contraception," *Graduate Nurses*, New York, 1938.
——— "The Moral Aspects of the Rh Factor," *The Linacre Quarterly*, January, 1947.
Shinners, J. *The Morality of Medical Experimentation on Living Human*

Subjects in the Light of Recent Papal Pronouncements, Washington, D.C.: The Catholic University of America Press, 1958.
Skelly, L.; Carty, C.; and Rumble, L. *Why Squander Illness?* (booklet), St. Paul, Minn.: Radio Replies Press, 1945.
Solesmes, Monks of, *The Human Body*, New York: Daughters of Saint Paul, 1960.
Spiritual Aid for Nurses and the Sick, Montreal: L'Oeuvre de Presse Dominicaine, 1944.
Splaine, J. *The Catholic Sick Room* (pamphlet), Glen Rock, N.J.: The Paulist Press, 1925.
Sullivan, J. *The Morality of Mercy Killing*, Westminster, Md.: The Newman Press, 1950.
Symposium on Birth Control, Washington, D.C.: National Catholic Welfare Conference, 1940.
VanderVeldt, J., and Odenwald, R. *Psychiatry and Catholicism*, New York: McGraw-Hill Book Company, 1952.
Walsh, W. T. *Babies, Not Bullets* (booklet), Glen Rock, N.J.: The Paulist Press, 1939.
Watson, M. *A Good Death* (pamphlet), Boston: Mission Church Press.
Woywod, S. "Excommunication in Cases of Abortion," *Homiletic and Pastoral Review*, December, 1935.
——— "Baptism of Infants in Hospitals," *Homiletic and Pastoral Review*, March, 1937.
——— "The Use of Morphine and Other Opiates in Death Agony," *Homiletic and Pastoral Review*, August, 1937.
——— "The Catholic Nurse Who Works for a Doctor Who Performs Operations and Gives Advice Contrary to Moral Law," *Homiletic and Pastoral Review*, August, 1937.
——— "Extreme Unction after 'Apparent' Death," *Homiletic and Pastoral Review*, May, 1939.
——— "Consent of Parents Required for Baptism of Children," *Homiletic and Pastoral Review*, January, 1941.

Sources of Medico-Moral Discourses of Pope Pius XII

Pope Pius XII delivered over ninety addresses in the medico-moral field. Some of these are on the general subject of health and proper care and nourishment of the body, others are addressed to the sick, others to hospital workers and those in allied fields, several to nurses, and a great number to doctors. Numerous ethical problems are squarely faced and clearly solved. Every one of these addresses is of value to a nurse. We list here some sources where many of them may be found in English translation.

The Pope Speaks, a quarterly of papal documents, 3622 Twelfth Street, N.E., Washington 17, D.C.

In pamphlet form, many of the Pope's addresses are published by The National Catholic Welfare Conference, 1312 Massachusetts Avenue, N.W., Washington 5, D.C., and by the Paulist Press, 21 Harristown Road, Glen Rock, N.J.

The Catholic Truth Society, London, England, prints a number of pamphlets and volumes containing selected addresses.

The Human Body is a one-volume compilation published by The Daughters of St. Paul, 50 St. Paul's Avenue, Boston 30, Mass.

Index

Numbers in italics indicate pages on which illustrations appear.